HISTORIC PHOTOGRAPHS

at the

NATIONAL MARITIME MUSEUM

An Illustrated Guide

National Maritime Museum

First published in 1995
by Ashford, Buchan & Enright publishers
Leatherhead, Surrey KT24 5HH

A CIP catalogue record for this book is available
from the British Library

ACKNOWLEDGEMENTS
This volume is the result of a sustained team effort across the Museum for several years, from the
early collection management and computerisation efforts to final publication.
It was researched, compiled and written by Bob Todd and David Hodge, curators of the
Historic Photographs Section, and Denis Stonham freelance author. The records compilation phase
was developed and managed by Fiona Elliott. Documentation support was provided
by Claire Brodie, Judi Hershon and Alan Wakefield. Iain MacKenzie, Guy Purdey and
David Taylor checked entries and advised. Pieter van der Merwe provided general editorial advice.
Photograph reproduction was by Tina Chambers and Peter Robinson and
photograph retrieval by Colin Starkey. The computerisation of the records was made
possible by Fran Laking and David Williams. The publication phase of the project
was managed by Karen Peart.
Thanks and appreciation to Rosa Botterill, Terry Corbett, Mike Bullions,
Roger Knight and David Spence of the National Maritime Museum
and to Debby Robson of The RD Consultancy and Philip Dalton for their invaluable ideas and support.

ISBN 1-85253-320-X

Layout and typesetting by Priory Publications
Haywards Heath, West Sussex

Printed in Great Britain by FotoDirect Ltd.
Brighton, East Sussex

Contents

FOREWORD by
Admiral of the Fleet The Lord Lewin KG GCB LVO DSC

The National Maritime Museum has over half a million historic photographs and the collection is still growing. To catalogue these individually is a task that Sisyphus might have found more satisfying than pushing his rock up hill, but similarly endless. Computer technology has recently enabled us to make faster progress but there is still a very long way to go. However, we are committed to improving the access to our vast collections and that is the purpose of this guide. We hope that maritime historians and those with a general interest in maritime history will enjoy browsing through its pages — and will find what they seek.

Most of the images in the guide have never been published. We are indebted to all those who over many years took the photographs and who then made them available to this important national collection. The 250 illustrations which accompany the text have been chosen to offer examples of the wide range of material available: they are but the tip of a very large iceberg.

Many people have contributed to the production of this book in different ways. To them all I offer congratulations on its realisation and I speak for all future readers when I give them our thanks.

Lewin of Greenwich

Chairman of Trustees

A Brief Explanation

Intended to cruise in the summer but maintain a Southampton to Cape Town service in winter, the liner *Astor* was acquired by the South African Marine Corporation in 1984. She was sold in August 1985 as her engines were not powerful enough to maintain a liner service. She is seen here in tow of the tug *Sun Thames* (1982) off Greenwich, on a cruise, in July 1985.
Collection: NMM NMM Neg. No. D969/2

Left: The White Star passenger liner *Majestic* was a product of the Belfast shipyard of Harland & Wolff in 1889. Together with nearly 500 First and Second Class passengers, the *Majestic* accommodated 1,000 in Third Class. This photograph was taken at Liverpool between 1903 and 1907.
Collection: Adams   NMM Neg. No. N19784

Below: The Canadian-Pacific liner *Empress of Asia* (1913) served on the Vancouver to Yokohama service, having accommodation for nearly 1,200 passengers, including 808 in the 'Asiatic steerage' class. This photograph was taken in the First Class Lounge soon after the vessel was completed.
Collection: Bedford Lemere NMM Neg. No. G10720

Facing page: Outward bound from Archangel to Port Natal with a deck cargo of timber, the turret-deck steamship *Walkure* (1907) called at Barry for bunkers in August 1908. A considerable quantity of coal was loaded onto the turret deck which caused the vessel to list and partially fill. The ship was later pumped out and resumed her voyage.
Collection: Shirvington NMM Neg. No. G3860

This is a guide to the negatives which comprise part of the Historic Photographs Collection at the National Maritime Museum. It both attempts to describe something of the nature and composition of the archive of photographs at Greenwich, and aims to facilitate access to its abundance of images. Overall, this volume should be considered as a primer and not be seen in any way as a full catalogue of the photographs in the collection, or as a systematic accounting of all the rich diversity which it contains.

The entries have been compiled from acquisition records prepared by the Museum's Documentation Section, information which is now being stored on a computer database but which is founded on earlier paper documentation. This programme has been supplementary to the steady but still incomplete subject cataloguing undertaken by the curators of the Historic Photographs Collection since 1960. The records of individual images held in the curatorial department are detailed and comprehensive for that proportion of the Collection which has so far undergone this fuller cataloguing process.

While this Guide provides an overview and introduction to parts of the Museum's archive of maritime photographs, such a work can only be representative rather than exhaustive. Access to the full riches of the collection should always be by initial enquiry to the relevant curators, stating the subject of interest. The best image to meet the requirement will then be selected utilising the much wider records available at the Museum. In other cases enquirers may be recommended to visit the department in person.

In addition to the negative collections described here, there are tens of thousands of photographic prints in the Historic Photographs Collection, each mounted, titled and arranged according to subject; there are also well over a thousand photograph albums. Prints exist from many of the negatives in this Guide, but by no means all, and many individual images from the albums have also been copied. A number of such albums figure in these pages.

The collection names under which the negatives are listed are those by which they have come to be known over the years within the Museum. They are to some extent arbitrary in origin and thus inconsistent, with collections named variously according to photographer, subject, ship or place, donor, or even (in at least one case) the home town of the donor! These names are not essential for finding particular photographs. Separate, comprehensive records relating to the acquisition of each group of negatives are held at the Museum and ensure systematic documentation of material received.

The collections of negatives comprise both original and copy material and are overwhelmingly on monochrome stock. However, there are increasingly large numbers of colour negatives and transparencies being accepted into the archive. Whenever possible, the most important of these are copied on to black and white negative stock, to increase versatility of use and to help ensure the greater permanence of images made originally with transitory colour dyes.

In selecting the photographs to illustrate this Guide, the intention has been to give as wide a representation as possible of the scope and variety of the images in the Collection. One or two illustrations have been chosen less for the quality of the photographs than for their subject matter; a few are from acquisitions not listed in these pages but which help to emphasise the richness of the holdings.

Concentrating essentially on the negative component of the archive means that a considerable proportion of the Museum's other photographs are omitted. None the less, this approach is perhaps the most useful for the researcher, who can now use this Guide to order prints directly from individual negatives. Serious students of maritime history in the age of photography will almost certainly wish, at some time, to visit the archive and discover the full wealth of pictorial documentation it contains.

During World War II large numbers of women joined the armed forces and carried out many of the maintenance tasks formerly undertaken by men. Here a member of the WRNS is operating a turning machine at a Royal Naval Depot.
Collection: Admiralty NMM Neg. No. AD15576

The Historical Background

Unmistakeably a 'blue-flue', this is Alfred Holt's Blue Funnel cargo liner *Automedon*, built by Vickers-Armstrong at Newcastle in 1949. This fine vessel belonged to a class which eventually comprised 21 ships, making good losses suffered by Holt's fleet during World War II.
Collection: Airfoto NMM Neg. No. P40436

Built for the Matson Line's San Francisco to Australia service, the turbine liner *Mariposa* (1931) is seen here in New Zealand waters during 1937. The *Mariposa* was not broken up until 1974, by which time she was Home Lines' *Homeric*.
Collection: Nautical Photo Agency NMM Neg. No. P11722

Harland & Wolff, Belfast, launched the turbine passenger liner *Edinburgh Castle* for the Union-Castle Line on 16 October 1947. With accommodation for 214 First Class and 541 Tourist Class passengers, the ship was employed regularly on the Southampton to Durban service.
Collection: Union-Castle NMM Neg. No. P39165

This remarkable photograph is of Brunel's iron screw-steamship *Great Britain* as she lay fitting-out by Brandon Wharf, Bristol during April or May 1844. In spite of some claims that this picture was made by Fox Talbot himself, it has not been possible to identify the photographer responsible for this extremely early photograph of the prototype of every merchant ship afloat today.
Collection: Talbot NMM Neg. No. 3758

A Victorian legacy

It is now exactly a century and a half since an unknown, early master of photography made the little negative image of Brunel's steamship *Great Britain* at Bristol. The photographer, one of the circle of William Henry Fox Talbot, the father of photography, would have been surprised to learn that 125 years later, on the return of the *Great Britain* to Bristol, his picture would be of immense value in planning the reconstruction of the vessel and that his negative would form part of a large collection of photographs held by a national museum devoted to British enterprise at sea.

Photographers of the early Victorian era, fascinated and engrossed by the opportunities and challenges of the new medium, could have had no intention of creating a fresh source of historical information. They would not have been conscious that their work would have permanent value to the historian by preserving for posterity a visual representation of the world about them. Maritime historians have good reason to be grateful that, in a number of instances, discriminating artistic eyes were attracted by a photogenic quality in the structure and appearance of ships in the mid-1840s and have left to us an invaluable photographic record of craft long passed from living memory. While the original motivation of one of these pioneer photographers, Richard Calvert Jones of Swansea, was a furtherance of his more general and enduring artistic vision and competence, perhaps the greatest value of his surviving photographs is that they constitute a meticulous historical account, quite distinct in the nature and quality of its reportage from any other type of archive source. His images stand today as considerable works of art in their own right.

The initial development of photography coincided with the Industrial Revolution going to sea. Photography itself stemmed directly from the burgeoning of new technologies, in terms of the application of chemistry and optics to picture-making, thus exploiting science in the production of art. For the maritime historian this is opportune. Generally speaking, development in

Above: In addition to his work on board passenger liners Bedford Lemere would accept commissions to photograph shipyards. This is one in a series of negatives made at the Clydebank yard of John Brown & Co Ltd in 1901.
Collection: Bedford Lemere
NMM Neg. No. G10577

Left: William Denny & Bros Ltd were shipbuilders and marine engineers. In the Dumbarton engine works on 18 October 1957 is a 6-cylinder Sulzer SD60 diesel for the pulpwood carrier *Elizabeth Bowater* and a 10-cylinder Sulzer 10TD36 diesel for the *Ionic Ferry.*
Collection: Denny
NMM Neg. No. P35461

maritime technology had been slow over the previous two centuries and a sailor of the mid-seventeenth century, transplanted to the 1840s, would soon have become accustomed to a sailing merchant vessel of the time. The trading vessels shown in photographs of the mid-nineteenth century give a strong impression of the way ships had looked and were constructed over the preceding two hundred years or so, and these images allow us a glance back at Georgian technology.

By 1844, when the photograph of the *Great Britain* was taken, steam propulsion was becoming common in the short-sea and coastal trades, and the steamship was establishing itself on ocean routes. The first regular passenger and mail service under steam on the Atlantic had been inaugurated only four years earlier, when Cunard's *Britannia* had left Liverpool for Halifax and Boston. Brunel's *Great Western* (the *Great Britain*'s predecessor) had crossed to New York in 1838, paddling her way there in a little over fifteen days. The *Great Britain* herself was a major milestone in the technological development of the steamship, being the first ocean-going, propeller-driven ship and the first large vessel to be built of iron; it is singularly fortunate that a photograph of her survives from so soon after she had left her building dock.

Looking forward from this date, early in Victoria's reign, photography provides us with a valuable visual record of technological development and social change in every instance of man's encounter with the sea. Photographs allow us to see how the techniques of small scale shipbuilding in wood, undertaken in ports widely spread along Britain's coastline, gave way first to building in iron, concentrating in locations close to sources of coal and iron ore, and then to steel, culminating in the construction of the gigantic ships with which the twentieth century has become familiar. The evolution of marine engineering can be traced by reference to photographs of early foundries and machine shops, where the millwright and blacksmith had developed their skills building engines for ships; then forward in time, using as evidence the photographic records left behind by once famous British shipbuilding enterprises, showing the engine shops, large as cathedrals, where the machinery of ships with names familiar to all were constructed. The human experience of seafaring and the life of the maritime communities over the last century and a half is brought most forcibly to our consciousness and understanding by the photograph, which can reveal the precise conditions in which men and women lived and worked during the rise and subsequent relative decline of British industrial predominance.

The photograph's commentary value to the historian is as a medium which is dispassionate and impartial, reflecting a situation with little or no prejudice or bias. The lens functions as a rigorous inquisitor which cannot itself permit omission or manipulation of the scene presented to it. The photographer may well have an interest in selecting his viewpoint, or choosing an opportune moment to give emphasis to, or omit, a particular feature. He thereby has some freedom to promote a cause or partisan intent, and the historian who uses photographs as source material must always assess this possibility. However, in the hands of the conscientious operator, the camera, in its mechanical appraisal and meticulous reportage of its subject, is unable to influence what it sees.

Any photographer witnessing an event has always to make decisions about what is worth recording and in this respect the historian is dependent on his (or her) qualities of sympathetic understanding and foresight. This is common, to some degree, to all classes of historical source material, where one would wish on the compiler all the benefits of hindsight! But it does not detract from the comprehensive and factual nature of the resultant pictorial record: the literalism of its historical account makes the photograph unique.

In comparison, it is not the aim of the artist in oils or water-colour to create an image of direct value as historical evidence and he feels free to interpret his subject accordingly. Ironically, of course, the majority of photographers have no intention of producing anything of lasting value when they use their cameras. When it is used in the cause of conscious and faithful documentation, the camera has a unique potential to allow us to witness an event almost as in life, permitting us to form some of the same opinions and judgements (tempered with due historical empathy) as we might had we been physically present.

The photograph can be approached as a rich source of historical detail, a moment in time frozen in perpetuity, allowing us to visit locations, examine structures and practices long vanished, encounter people in their historical environment and context, and develop insights and awareness otherwise inaccessible to us.

The peculiar quality of photographs to be infinitely reproducible puts the information they contain into as many hands as desire it, at negligible trouble and cost. On the one hand, they are part of the trivia of the twentieth century: commonplace, familiar to all and within the means and competence of everyone to create. On the other hand, though frequently found faded or torn, previously disregarded and considered worthless, many photographs can be considered as small documents of history. The best are certainly worthy of inclusion in those national collections to which their subjects relate.

The National Maritime Museum's collection: foundation

The formation of such a collection of nautical photographs had been one of the objects of the National Maritime Museum at its foundation in 1934, making it a pioneer among national museums, both in recognising the historic value of the photographic image and according historic photographs a high degree of importance for research. The Museum opened to the public in 1937 and some 5,000 negatives had already been collected when the outbreak of war in 1939 closed

Above: A large merchant sailing ship towing into the East India Docks, London, on 4 June 1898.
Collection: Adams NMM Neg. No. N19713

Facing page, top: The National Maritime Museum was opened by King George VI on 27 April 1937, as one of the first official acts of his reign. This photograph records the scene in Neptune Hall. In the platform party was Princess (later Queen) Elizabeth.
Collection: NMM NMM Neg. No. C9138A

Facing page, bottom: The first steam drifter to be built at Lowestoft was completed in 1897. By 1903 there were 100 such vessels registered at the port. The *Smilax* (LT594) was typical of these sturdy fishermen and was built at Lowestoft in 1910. She is seen here at Scarborough passing, in the foreground, a local coble.
Collection: Gunnersbury Museum NMM Neg. No. P1147

it again and brought such activity to a halt. On the return of peace, however, thoughts could once more turn to developing the Museum's collections, the most important of which had been removed to safe storage outside London during hostilities.

The Society for Nautical Research (SNR) had been founded in 1910 to encourage research into matters relating to seafaring and shipbuilding in all ages, one of its principal aims being the establishment of a national museum dedicated to recording the history of Britain's relationship with the sea. The Society played a key role in founding the National Maritime Museum and has maintained the closest links with it. At the Annual General Meeting of the Society, held at the Museum on 16 July 1947, a proposal that a sub-committee be formed to collaborate with the Museum in collecting photographs of maritime interest was eagerly adopted. The Photographic Records Sub-Committee of the SNR was the idea of Basil Greenhill, a leading authority on merchant sailing vessels and one who recognised the value of the photograph in documenting the rapidly vanishing boat types and trading vessels under sail related to the British Isles. Dr Greenhill was to become the Director of the National Maritime Museum in 1967 and did much to develop its historic photographs collection, promoting the notion of photographs as valuable historical source material.

The SNR's Photographic Records Sub-Committee quickly got into its stride under the chairmanship of Alan Villiers, whose well-known contributions to maritime history and marine photography need no rehearsal here, not least since his own collection of photographs is documented in these pages. Also serving on the committee were Basil Greenhill and H. Oliver Hill. Oliver Hill is remembered with admiration and gratitude for his deep knowledge of the small craft which, under sail and oar, traded out of the smallest ports of the United Kingdom and the near continent. By means of these boats and vessels, maritime communities made a living from the sea and its harvest, before the internal-combustion engine forever relegated sail to the yachtsman. The magnificent collection of photographs of these utilitarian distinctive and often handsome craft which Hill amassed, taking the majority himself, forms a further part of the National Maritime Museum's archive: it too is listed here. In addition to the members appointed from the Society, Michael Robinson, the first Keeper of Pictures at the Museum, was co-opted to the committee. The task of arranging and cataloguing the photographs as they arrived at Greenwich initially fell to his staff.

The joint aim of the SNR and the Museum was to create a comprehensive photographic account of every aspect of human endeavour at sea: in trade or war, whether exploiting the sea for its resources or simply going to sea as a means of recreation. As it was ambitiously expressed at the time, the intention was 'to draw together a complete record of the development of steam and sailing ships and of life at sea since the first days of photography'. It should be emphasised that for this purpose both the Society and the Museum regarded photography simply as a means for gathering and presenting information in a comprehensive accessible form. No regard was given to representing marine photography as a genre, or as a means of artistic expression.

No readily identifiable school of marine photography emerged during the nineteenth century, although many images from that time demonstrate a sensitive appreciation of the subject, comparable to that which characterises some marine painting. A major reason for this, no doubt, is that the technical limitations of the craft for most of the century rendered photography incapable of capturing the restless movements associated with wind and wave, which were then more successfully the province of the marine

---

Facing page:

Top: The foreshore of the River Dovey at Aberdovey about 1895. The topsail schooner *Ann Warren* of Aberystwyth, built in 1857, is waiting to refloat on the tide.
Collection: Frith NMM Neg. No. G4320

Bottom left: The Thos. & Jas. Harrison cargo liner *Collegian* of 1899 at sea during World War I. Her boats are swung out ready for use. She was lost to submarine attack in October 1917.
Collection: The Nautical Photo Agency NMM Neg. No. N47896

Bottom right: The wreck of the *Preussen* (1902), the only five-masted ship ever built. The *Preussen* went ashore under the South Foreland in November 1910 following collision with the Newhaven to Dieppe steamer *Brighton* and broke her back.
Collection: Nautical Photo Agency NMM Neg. No. P533

Above: HMS *Warrior* was the world's first deep-sea, iron-built and armoured warship and was launched in 1860. Seen here at Plymouth, probably in 1862, she is now one of the main attractions of the Portsmouth Naval Heritage Centre.
Collection: Perkins NMM Neg. No. N5180

Right: Looking aft along the port side of the *Passat* (1911) at sea under sail on 9 March 1949. Anne Stanley, made fast to the mizzen shrouds, is at work with her camera.
Collection: Stanley NMM Neg. No. P8479

Below: One of a series of 340 negatives taken on board the destroyer HMS *Hampshire* on the completion of her fitting out in March 1963 at John Brown's Clydebank shipyard. This is the gas turbine room at 4 Deck level.
Collection: Admiralty NMM Neg. No. N38776

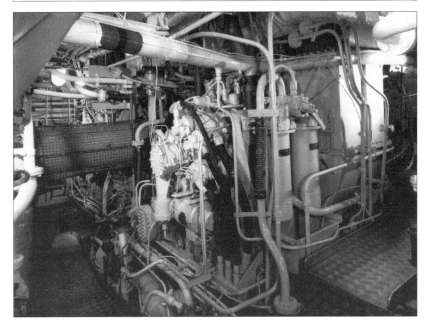

painter. The resulting preoccupation with documentary content still characterises the National Maritime Museum's collection of historic photographs today.

The SNR was aware that, spread about the coasts of Britain, 'in inns and cottages, in local museums and, above all, in photographers' shops', there were thousands of photographs taken in the course of the previous century which showed docks, harbours and shipbuilding yards, local ships and shipowners. Very often in the past, such photographs had been lost on the death of their owners. Too often, complete collections of photographs of great but unrecognised historical value had been destroyed when a local photographer closed his business. Without any central repository to which redundant photographs of maritime interest might be sent (even if an awareness of the images' value had been present) a wealth of pictorial evidence had been discarded over the years. In particular, with the gradual decline of British shipbuilding, the records of many shipbuilding companies have disappeared. The stories of large glass negatives being stripped of their emulsion and used to glaze greenhouses are not entirely apocryphal. Members of the SNR were asked to prevent this sort of disaster occurring and to inform the Sub-Committee of any known nautical photographs that might sooner or later be incorporated into the Museum's collection. The first task of the Photographic Records Sub-Committee, working through the SNR and its journal 'The Mariner's Mirror', was to make people aware that photographs were being sought and to ask the owners of collections to consider giving or leaving them to the Museum, or lending them so that they might be copied. All members were urged to help the work by letting it be known that the building-up of a central collection had begun. The Society

The four-masted barque *Parma* (1902) at sea, homeward-bound from Port Victoria, Australia in 1933. This photograph was taken from the port bowsprit guy, looking aft at the bow and forecastle head.
Collection: Villiers NMM Neg. No. N61380

Above: The Iranian tanker *Shirvan* (1979) was hit by an Iraqi missile whilst at Kharg Island in September 1987 during the Iran-Iraq war. She is seen here in January 1988 at Singapore, awaiting repairs.
Collection: Airfoto
NMM Neg. No. P44623

Top left: Crew members of the barque *Parma* (1902) work in the water filling the deck as the ship pitches in heavy weather on passage in 1932–33. Life-lines and nettings have been rigged for the crew's safety.
Collection: Villiers
NMM Neg. No. N61442

Centre left: The three-masted barque *William Miles* was built in Bristol in 1816 and is typical of the merchant ships of the period. She was wrecked in 1883. She is here seen, probably in a Sussex port, near the end of her career.
Collection: Nautical Photo Agency
NMM Neg. No. P6874

Bottom left: A spritsail barge on the Sussex Ouse. These double-ended craft carried a variety of bulk cargoes such as chalk or clay between Lewes, the county town of East Sussex, and the port of Newhaven. Some larger barges of this type made short coastal voyages with cement.
Collection: H Oliver Hill
NMM Neg. No. P73901

also published news of the appeal in maritime trade and technical journals, and in yachting magazines.

In October 1948 'The Mariner's Mirror' reported on the progress of this appeal, of which the result had been most unexpected. Alan Villiers announced, with delight, that results had been beyond the greatest hopes. Already between four and five thousand photographs had been rescued, as he put it, which might otherwise easily have been lost. A wave of material had flowed in, arriving at the Museum sometimes at a rate of hundreds of photographs per week and rapidly overwhelming immediate methodical arrangement of the images. The custodians of the collection were none the less surprised and pleased to find that they now held photographs of several types of craft which had been extinct for some time, and of which it was thought very little knowledge existed. The photographs were already making it possible to discover exactly how these craft had been constructed, rigged and used. Special thanks to Basil Greenhill were recorded for initiating the process and for helping to carry it forward.

As the collection grew, the small number of staff in the Print Room at the Museum, who had taken on the responsibility for it in addition to their other duties, were gradually able to gain control of the inward flood of images and to assess the strengths and weaknesses of the growing archive. The Museum's photographic studio had also worked hard and by 1950 it became practical to make, with minimum delay, copy negatives from small numbers of prints loaned to the Museum. Those illustrating the work and living conditions of seamen were especially sought. So too were photographs of cargo handling and of small working and fishing boats representative of the wide variety of types in use throughout the world. It was stressed that the Museum was less concerned with the quality of a photograph than with its subject.

At this date over 50,000 photographs had entered the Museum, this number including the important Gould collection of nineteenth-century negatives taken at Gravesend and the series of nearly 300 photographs taken aboard the four-masted barque *Passat* during her last voyage to Australia in 1949. The latter were the work of Anne Stanley, who took them at the request of the Society for Nautical Research. On 4 October 1950 an exhibition of nautical photographs drawn from those so far collected opened to the public at the

Museum and subsequently travelled to Bristol, Cardiff and Edinburgh. In July 1951, when the collection had grown to 70,000 photographic prints, it was estimated that negatives from which prints could be made to order existed for half that number of images, indicating a satisfyingly high level of public access to the archive.

From these beginnings the historic photographs collection at the Museum has grown tremendously; it now numbers well over half a million photographs and over 1,300 photograph albums, in addition to the negatives described in this Guide. George Osbon, the first curator recruited to work solely on the collection, was appointed in 1960. Osbon devised the systems of categorising each photograph which remain the basis of work on the archive today.

At its peak the Historic Photographs Section employed four curators cataloguing and describing the subject of each photographic negative, and facilitating access to the great wealth of information which the collection contains. Today the collection still depends mainly on donations of photographs to broaden its record of maritime affairs. It is therefore remarkable, as well as fortunate, that necessary reliance on a pattern of acquisition so much open to chance and good fortune has resulted in a record substantially complete in it scope, representing as it does most aspects of man's use of the sea.

A subject overview

The progress of naval architecture over the course of 150 years is amply described in considerable and comprehensive collections of ship portraits. The warship, in particular, has changed dramatically during that time, emphasising perhaps more than any other development in ship design and function the pace and nature of technological innovation, experimentation and fulfilment in nineteenth century shipbuilding. Early in 1845 the 'Navy List' recorded 113 steam vessels in Royal Naval service, but not one belonged to the battle fleet. In 1846 the *Ajax*, a 60-gun ship of the line, bearing a strong resemblance to two-deckers of the eighteenth century, was undocked to become the Royal Navy's first steam line-of-battle ship. Her engine drove the ship at seven knots, sufficient for manoeuvring power, but the *Ajax* had a full sailing rig and when under sail her funnel was lowered and her screw hoisted out of the water. The three-deckers *Duke of Wellington* and *Marlborough*, of 1852 and 1855 respectively, were laid down as pure sailing ships and fitted with engines and boilers when building was well advanced. Both ships were built of wood and it was not until 1860 that the first iron-clad capital ship in the Royal Navy, the *Warrior,* was launched on the Thames. The *Warrior* was revolutionary, with iron armour that made the vessel practically immune to hostile fire, although her design retained masts and sails. During the 1860s, 1870s and 1880s, there followed a bewildering variety of capital ships, as the proponents of the broadside vessel tussled with those who favoured the turret and tried out their designs in practice; on one occasion with disastrous result, when the top-heavy turret ship *Captain* capsized in 1870. Developments in armament also influenced the appearance of ships built to carry and use each new type of gun. The twentieth century began with the conception of the *Dreadnought,* which, both as a particular ship and a general design, was even more revolutionary in her superiority of armament and protection, and introduced the characteristic visual profile of the capital ship of the new century.

These changes and the course of further evolution towards the most modern vessels of today can be traced in the historic photographs collection. There is a representative coverage of the ships of overseas navies but, naturally, it is the vessels of the Royal Navy which predominate in the archive. At the centre of the collection of warship photographs are more than 12,000 negatives brought together by Richard Perkins with the aim of portraying the evolution of the ship of war during the period from 1860 to just after World War II. All classes of vessel are represented, from the smallest yard craft to the capital ship. The Perkins Collection is complemented and its range extended by a number of smaller collections; some of ship portraits, others taken during the service careers of particular vessels. Among the latter might be mentioned the negatives given by Captain P. L. Gunn and taken aboard the cruiser HMS *Aurora* between 1915 and 1917, and the similar collection depicting the destroyer *Laforey* during the same period.

Together with ship portraits, there are important collections of photographs showing ships under construction. These are listed individually in the Guide but brief mention should be made here of the important group of negatives showing the *Dreadnought* of 1906 from keel-laying to dry-docking and, as an example of modern warship building, more than 1,000 negatives taken of the

guided missile destroyer HMS *Hampshire* during the course of construction between 1959 and 1963. The life and work of the officers and men of HM ships is not neglected. One very early negative shows a seaman at the wheel of HMS *Superb* in 1845, standing alongside a marine sentry, and his later nineteenth and twentieth century counterparts feature in many photographs of 'Jack' on board and ashore.

The merchant ship underwent a transformation during the nineteenth century as the increasing potential of the new techniques of shipbuilding in iron and steel, the developing skill of the marine engine builder and the demands of changing patterns of trade all exerted their influence. Arguably, the merchant sailing ship evolved more quickly in the second half of the century than in the previous two and this is fully documented in photographs held in the collection. The large iron, and later steel, sailing ship with up to four and even five masts was conceived, refined and superseded as steam propulsion became more efficient and economical. Few sailing vessels were built after 1900 and there are, regrettably, even fewer images of the very large vessels under construction, but very many other sailing ship portraits exist.

During the latter part of the last century, when a few British square-riggers operated as cargo-carrying training ships, and were still taking passengers to Australia, small cameras were available which accepted reasonably fast, glass-plate negatives or even roll-film. From about 1890 it became possible to carry a camera into situations and locations in which the photographer had hitherto found it difficult to work. Photography was becoming more accessible to the amateur and several series of remarkable pictures, taken at sea aboard the last generation of merchant sailing ships, have found their way into the archive at Greenwich. Some of these photographs were taken by passengers but there are others, taken on voyages of the very last of these ships, made by members of the crew.

The most notable photographs in this class are those taken by Alan Villiers between 1919 and 1936. Attracted as a young boy by the big sailing merchantmen which called at the port of Melbourne, where he lived, Villiers eventually resolved to go to sea himself, signing aboard the barque *Rothesay Bay* in 1919. Ten years later, after service in a number of ships, including a whaling voyage and after a spell ashore working as a journalist, Villiers formed the notion of joining a square-rigger and making a cine-film record of a Cape Horn sailing ship. Always a committed and competent photographer, the visual record he has left in film and photograph is one of the most important sources concerned with the last tall ships. It forms a rich legacy of some of the most powerful and evocative images ever taken at sea.

In addition to these photographs and those of Anne Stanley, there is a remarkable set of images made by the Second Mate of the barque *Garthsnaid* on a voyage from Iquique to Delagoa Bay soon after World War I; these came to the Museum with the collection of the Nautical Photo Agency. Among the *Garthsnaid* pictures is the photograph which has, perhaps, come to symbolise the Museum's collection of historic photographs, showing members of the crew making fast the foresail in a gale, as seen from the end of the jib-boom. This is unquestionably one of the finest photographs, if not the finest, taken aboard a deep-sea, square-rigged merchant vessel in heavy weather. These photographs preserve the memory of a generation of seafarers whose surpassing skills of seamanship were rarely met once the big sailing ship had vanished. They are testimony to a way of life at sea, alien to current experience.

Commemoration of the coasting sailing vessels and fishing craft of the British Isles may be found, particularly, in the negatives made and collected by H. Oliver Hill. Hill's purpose was to record as much detail as possible of the construction and use of these distinctive types of small vessel, and to preserve some impression of the life of those who sailed in them. Other collections concentrate more specifically on the craft of particular areas, especially the south of England and Scotland. There are important groups of negatives of craft in foreign waters, particularly those of the Arabian peninsula and China. The former are represented in the fine photographs taken by Lt. Cdr. Vaughan in the late 1920s and, most notably again, by Alan Villiers, who made several voyages in types of Arab dhow before World War II. Craft of the China Seas, the junk and sampan types of the Chinese coast and southwards to Singapore and Penang, are documented in the Waters negatives taken late in the 1930s.

Steamships of the world's fleets, and later motor-vessels, from the earliest days of photography to

Looking aft from the bowsprit of the barque *Garthsnaid* (1892) on passage in heavy weather from Iquique to Delagoa Bay in 1920. Four of the crew are aloft on the foreyard, securing the sail.
Collection: Nautical Photo Agency NMM Neg. No. P7148

the present are to be found in great numbers in the photographs held by the Museum. It is possible to follow the development of the merchant steamship from its origins as a small packet vessel, uneconomical in operation and suited only to the high-grade traffic of passengers and mails, to the enormous vessels of today, moving up to half a million tons of commodities in bulk on each voyage. The increasing momentum of mid-nineteenth century commercial activity demanded a means of overseas passenger transport that was capable of achieving some degree of predictability and of running to an approximate timetable. It also required resolution of the problem of delivering raw materials and goods without the costly delays and frustrations to which sailing vessels were subject.

Brunel's vision of extending the Great Western Railway from Bristol to New York, with a regular steamship service, was realised on completion of the *Great Western*, the first steamship designed specifically for the North Atlantic run. This was to become the most lucrative and prestigious service for shipowners and the rise of the Atlantic liner, its changing appearance and propulsion, and the increasingly sumptuous interior appointments can be followed in photographs taken over the ensuing century. In the general trades, the steam-driven cargo ship began to break the monopoly of sail when engineering genius and skill had advanced sufficiently to build engines that were efficient in operation and reliable in service. Photographs of these forerunners of today's ocean giants and of the precursors of the Ultra Large Crude Carriers, which are the largest modern tankers of the present, are to be found in the collection, together with images of every merchant ship type of the intervening period.

By far the largest group of photographic negatives of merchant steam and sailing ships is

The P & O liner *Rome* was built at Greenock in 1881 for her owners' Australia service but in 1891, whilst being re-engined, a serious fire destroyed much of her accommodation. This photograph shows the First Class Dining Saloon after refitting, in January 1892.
Collection: Bedford Lemere NMM Neg. No. G10510

that of the Nautical Photo Agency. The 30,000 negatives which comprise this collection is the largest single acquisition of such images received by the National Maritime Museum and constitute an immensely rich source for the maritime historian. In gathering together the photographs it was the intention of Frank Bowen and Captain Fred Poyser to represent, as far as possible, every aspect of ships and seafaring during the age of photography. They are to be congratulated that this object was achieved so magnificently and it is a matter of deep satisfaction and gratitude that the photographs of the agency were deposited in a national collection following Captain Poyser's death in 1966. Those negatives of warships which once formed part of the Nautical Photo Agency are now in a private archive, and negatives which were only on loan were returned.

The Nautical Photo Agency collection covers the period to the mid-1950s. Complementing it are a number of smaller collections of images, among the earlier of which is the Gould collection. Showing vessels lying at Gravesend on the Thames, this is particularly fine and numbers some two and a half thousand negatives dating from the 1870s. Among the vessels depicted are Blackwall frigates – passenger-carrying sailing ships which were direct descendants of the East Indiamen of the previous century. It also shows their immediate successors, similar in appearance but steam-driven, with a funnel between the masts. There are photographs of early tankers in the Gould collection and of liners of the 1880s, taking aboard passengers for Australia. Passenger liner interiors of the period c.1890–1920 are the subject of the 500 negatives taken by the firm of professional photographers, Bedford Lemere. These are large, glass negatives of stunning quality and depict much of the extravagance and opulence of premier passenger ship accommodation, together with an occasional glimpse of that reserved for passengers travelling in the lowest class. Also in the Bedford Lemere collection is a magnificent group of negatives of the liner *Aquitania*, of 1914, under construction on the Clyde.

Major representation of merchant shipping from the 1950s to 1980s is to be found in the negatives acquired from Airfoto. This firm of professional aerial photographers operated in the Strait of Malacca and photographed ships passing through the strait for the benefit of shipowners and ships' crews. Many specialised collections of photographs complete the documentation of

merchant shipping since the 1840s. Among these, as examples, might be mentioned those negatives donated by the P & O Steam Navigation Company and the Union-Castle Mail Steamship Company. Among the photographs devoted to British fishing vessels are the 700 negatives taken by J. A. Tvedt in the 1970s and 1980s.

The photographs of merchant shipbuilding activity in the collection includes negatives from the archives of shipbuilding firms. The most important of these are some 2,000 which were made for William Denny & Brothers' shipyard at Dumbarton. Denny's built the first large steel ship, the *Rotomahana* in 1879, and from about that time had a policy of taking photographs of all vessels built by the firm at progressive stages of construction. Sadly, most of the resulting negatives were destroyed but what remains constitutes a valuable record of shipyard activity in the late nineteenth and twentieth centuries until the yard's closure in 1963. A comparable collection is that received from the firm of Vosper Thornycroft Ltd, comprising nearly 8,000 negatives showing ship and boat building and repair work carried out by John I. Thornycroft & Co at Chiswick, Hampton, Woolston and Northam from the 1860s to the 1950s.

Although interesting locations frequently appear in photographs, the main subject of which may be a ship portrait or which may concentrate on some

The propelling machinery of the torpedo boat destroyer *Daring* in the Chiswick workshops of John I Thornycroft & Co Ltd in 1893. This was 'a modification of Mr Humphry's four cylinder triple expansion engine'. Two sets of this machinery were installed.
Collection: Thornycroft NMM Neg. No. G12841

Above: The two-masted topsail schooner *Dispatch* of Whitby was built at Stockton in 1806. She is here seen moored inside the breakwater at Broadstairs, Kent about 1887.
Collection: Frith
NMM Neg. No. G4274

Left: Discharging cargo from the trading smack *Malvina*, built in 1872 and of only 17 net tons, on the beach at Kildonan, on the Isle of Arran in the Firth of Clyde, on 6 August 1908.
Collection: MacFee
NMM Neg. No. N29857

particular activity or object ashore, there are in the Museum's collection a large number of primarily topographical photographs. The negatives which were formerly part of the Francis Frith archive of British landscape and coastal views form the core of this element. These professionally-made glass negatives show maritime Britain in the last two decades of the Victorian era and in the period up to the outbreak of World War II. Produced essentially for the visitor and holiday market, and therefore selective in their subject matter, the Frith negatives are nevertheless a fascinating and fertile source for social as well as maritime historians.

Middle-class Victorian and Edwardian curiosity regarding those whose living was from the sea was satisfied by photographs of coastal communities at work, and portrait studies of fishermen and their families. Additional collections of negatives of coastal scenes, particularly those of S. C. Fox and Miss K. J. MacFee (the latter concentrating on Scottish scenes) are the work of accomplished amateur photographers. Created for personal motives, such material benefits from more spontaneity and vigour than the carefully composed pictures made by the Frith firm. Overseas locations do not feature extensively in negatives held at the Museum although three small groups of negatives are worthy of mention; these are devoted to the National Antarctic Expedition

of 1901–04 and the research voyage to the whaling grounds off South Georgia and the Southern Orkneys during 1925–27. On both occasions the research ship *Discovery* was used.

The historic photographs collection at the National Maritime Museum is, generally speaking, not one of prime significance to the student of the history of photography. There are, however, a number of items of outstanding importance and of sufficient general interest that merit description.

All the major photographic processes developed since the mid-nineteenth century are represented in the collection. The very earliest photographic process capable of making permanent pictures, produced on a light-sensitive, coated metal surface, was devised by the Parisian, Louis Daguerre, in 1839. Called the Daguerreotype, it gave a direct positive image which was incapable of being reproduced and so had no long-term future. There are only a few images of this type in the collection.

The advance which led the way to photography in the form we recognise today was the perfection of a practicable negative-positive process by William Henry Fox Talbot in 1840. This technique, which Fox Talbot named calotype (from the Greek word *kalos* meaning beautiful), utilised a paper base for the light-sensitive salts. To reverse the image, from negative to positive, a

The main deck of a merchant sailing ship of the first half of the nineteenth century, looking aft towards the poop. This photograph, made on a paper negative, was taken c.1845.
Collection: Talbot NMM Neg. No. C2259

further sheet of sensitised paper would be put into close contact with the first, which had been waxed to render it translucent, and exposed to light. The most valuable feature of the calotype was that an unlimited number of positive copies could be made from the initial negative image. There are 34 calotype negatives and 24 positives in the Museum collection. These images are the greatest treasure in the photograph archive and were acquired through the generosity of Miss Matilda Talbot, the granddaughter of Fox Talbot. The photographs are from the collection previously held at Lacock Abbey, home of Miss Talbot and, earlier, of Fox Talbot himself. Many of the images were made by the Reverend Calvert Richard Jones, a close associate of Fox Talbot, whose artistic talent as a painter in watercolours was transferred to photography. The negatives made at Swansea, showing vessels sitting on the mud in the harbour,

are very likely to have been made by Calvert Jones. He is also known to have been in Malta at the end of 1845 and early in 1846 and the few views of Grand Harbour which feature among these negatives are almost certainly his work. It is also likely that some of the photographs are by Nicolaas Henneman, another illustrious name from the beginnings of photography.

A great step forward was taken in 1851, the year of the Great Exhibition in London celebrating progress in the arts and sciences, when Frederick Scott Archer announced a new photographic technique. His process was able to use a glass base for the light-sensitive coating, thus producing negatives of greater clarity than the earlier, paper-based, calotype. The light-sensitive salts were held on the glass by collodion (gun-cotton dissolved in ether and alcohol) and exposed in the camera while still wet, since the emulsion rapidly lost its sensitivity to light in drying. The collodion, or wet-plate, negative had all the clarity of detail of the earlier Daguerreotype but the disadvantage of requiring all the paraphernalia of the darkroom on hand whenever and wherever the wet-plates were to be exposed.

Many examples of negatives using this process are to be found in the Gould collection, the earliest dating from 1871. From these it is apparent that the speed (or sensitivity to light) of the photographic emulsion had increased since Fox Talbot produced the calotype. Calvert Jones had no choice but to photograph ships at low water, lying dried-out, since it would have been impossible, given the long exposure time then needed, to make the photographs whilst the ships were afloat and moving gently at their moorings. Gould's negatives are not entirely free from movement of image but in the photographs taken by the wet-plate process it is the water of the river which is seen to lack definition. The wet collodion negative was used by such early documentary photographers as Roger Fenton, whose photographs taken in the Crimea during the war of 1854–56 made him the first war photographer, and Francis Frith who, between 1856 and 1860, produced hundreds of photographs in Egypt, Syria and the Holy Land using the process. Sadly, no original example of Frith's work from this period is among his negatives at the Museum.

The introduction of gelatine as the base of a photographic emulsion dates from 1871 when Richard Leach Maddox suggested the technique. By 1879 it was possible to purchase factory-

Here seen lying at Gravesend with a cargo of coal is the Thames sailing barge *Connaught*, of 1879. She is rigged as a stumpie, having no topmast or topsail.
Collection: Gould NMM Neg. No. G1660

Top: The Thames sailing barge *Unity*, bringing a cargo of hay into London. Stack cargoes such as this fed the thousands of horses in nineteenth-century London, the inevitable by-product being taken away by sailing barge to fertilise the fields producing the next hay crop.
Collection: Thacker
NMM Neg. No. 3055

Middle: On her completion in 1892 the paddle steamer *Koh-i-noor* was the fastest river steamer in Britain, capable of 20 knots. She ran on the Thames between London Bridge, Southend and Clacton and is seen here on 13 August 1906. Note the very exposed bridge for the officers and helmsman.
Collection: Adams
NMM Neg. No. N19776

Bottom: Merchant seamen shipping aboard a sailing ship in the nineteenth century were often allowed one month's wages in advance for clothes and gear. For the first month of the voyage they were, therefore, 'flogging a dead horse' and at the end of that time the passing of the Dead Horse could be celebrated. This scene, on the ship *John O'Gaunt* (1869), shows the unfortunate 'horse' shortly before its ritual disposal overboard.
Collection: Nautical Photo Agency
NMM Neg. No. P7263

31

manufactured dry plates which could easily be handled by the amateur. Sensitivity was much increased over previous processes and exposures of 1/25 of a second were possible in good light. With this innovation, the art of photography passed from being an almost exclusively professional activity into the hands of any amateur of modest competence. Many examples of early gelatine-based negatives are included in the historic photographs collection, demonstrating the versatility of both photography and photographer in the 1880s and 1890s. Glass plates measuring only a few inches square, with correspondingly small cameras, could be taken into any situation where there was sufficient light for an exposure to be made. Many scenes of shipboard life in the late nineteenth century were recorded by this means.

Photography was revolutionised once more in 1889, when George Eastman produced a satisfactory transparent celluloid film coated with a gelatine emulsion for his new Kodak camera. Together with a comprehensive developing and printing service which he had set up, the new roll-film enabled Eastman to claim that his camera could be operated by anyone who had sufficient intelligence to point a box straight and press a button: 'you press the button, we do the rest'. Photography was now accessible to all and the universal appeal and adoption of the pursuit is reflected in the content of the historic photographs collection at Greenwich, which is predominantly amateur in origin. Many of the photographs were taken with no greater intention on the part of the photographer than creating personal mementos of an experience or location. Other practitioners, among them Alan Villiers, were acutely aware of a world passing away and, as we have seen, took photographs with a sense of historical record.

In the case of Britain, dependence on the sea for national security and prosperity has been absolute. Yet the experience of those who make their living on and from the sea has long been remote from most people's understanding and the seaman, with his distinctive craft and customs, an enigmatic figure. To some extent at least, the camera has brought us into close contact with the actuality of that human experience and with the conditions and means under and by which men and women have conducted their relationship with the sea.

It is part of the responsibility of any institution which holds an archive of photographs of the quality and importance of the National Maritime Museum's to promote it as a source for historians, and to facilitate and inspire its use. Many of the images in the collection have been published over the years and in the last two decades several books based on the Museum's photographs have appeared. The most recent of these, John Falconer's 'Sail and Steam' (Viking, 1993), presented a century of seafaring enterprise through more than 200 photographs drawn from the collection. Earlier, in 1981, 'Seafaring under Sail', by Basil Greenhill and Denis Stonham (Patrick Stephens), told the story of the merchant seaman in 123 photographs from the archive. 'The Royal Navy Day by Day' by A. B. Sainsbury (Ian Allan, 1992) contains over 250 prints and many images from the historic photographs collection have been used in gallery displays at the Museum and in a number of exhibitions devoted entirely to historic maritime photographs. Two catalogues, listing negatives of warships and merchant sailing ships respectively, were published in 1967 and 1976. Each give comprehensive details of individual photographs from collections described in the present volume. (These catalogues are currently out of print.)

To reiterate, this Guide is not intended to provide a specific answer to the question: 'do you have a photograph of . . . .?' but within these pages the reader will find a general account of each group of negatives, the circumstances of its acquisition by the Museum and a brief indication of content. The 250 photographs which accompany the text have been chosen to represent the collection as a whole and to give an impression of the nature and quality of the material found in it. In making the selection, the intention has been to offer examples from the wide range of subject matter available and to include a specimen photograph from most of the individual collections listed in the Guide. A few of the photographs are examples from collections which, for various reasons, will not be found listed in the text. Naturally, the overall strengths of the collection are emphasised in the chosen illustrations and many images may be well-known or have been widely published elsewhere. For this no apology is made, since in a definitive Guide, which this seeks to be, the sin of omission is greater than that of inclusion.

Main Subjects

This photograph is produced from a calotype negative believed to be the work of Nicolaas Henneman. It shows the poop and quarterdeck of the 2nd Rate ship-of-the-line HMS *Superb* in September 1845 at Plymouth.
Collection: Talbot NMM Neg. No. C3596

The 6th Destroyer Flotilla, Atlantic Fleet, demonstrating the effectiveness of a smokescreen during manoeuvres about 1929. The *Westcott*, built by Denny Bros at Dumbarton in 1917–18, is making her contribution.
Collection: Perkins NMM Neg. No. N42141

HM *MTB 24* alongside her sister *MTB 25* in the Thornycroft shipyard at Northam on the River Itchen on 10 July 1941. Other naval craft include three French VTBs and the British *CMB 104*, a minelaying coastal motor boat built in 1921.
Collection: Thornycroft NMM Neg. No. G5654

Warship Photographs

The core element of the visual documentation of warships comprises 12,000 negatives given to the Museum by Richard Perkins in 1967. Perkins selected the negatives which entered his main collection to demonstrate the major changes in appearance which each ship underwent in the course of its service career. Negatives which duplicated others, showing a vessel in a particular configuration, or which were of inferior quality, Perkins relegated to his reserve collection. This distinction was apparent in the list of the Perkins negatives published by the Museum in 1967, which included all those of the main collection but only a representative selection from the reserve collection. No such discrimination is observed among the prints from these negatives which are housed in the Historic Photographs Section, all photographs of any particular ship being stored together.

Perkins's ambition to record the various alterations to a ship, as differing requirements of service, improved armament or outfit progressively changed her original appearance, was achieved most fully for major warships of the Royal Navy. There are quite comprehensive series of photographs which show these changes, especially of capital ships, and sometimes in detail. In many cases of more minor vessels, sufficient photographs could not be found or taken by Perkins to document fully a ship's career. In the case of ships of the nineteenth century, Royal Navy photographs were, naturally, quite rare or simply unobtainable. Warships of foreign navies are included in the Perkins negatives but comprehensive documentation is reserved for the Royal Navy.

To accompany and explain his collection and its purpose, Perkins compiled a series of albums in which, by means of his own profile drawings, he described how all types of Royal Naval vessel evolved during the second half of the nineteenth century and the first half of the twentieth. These albums are a rich source for the naval historian.

The Perkins collection is an example of an archive of photographs compiled for a particular purpose. It is complemented in the Collection by more randomly composed groups of negatives, all of which will be found listed here. These mostly smaller collections generally fall into four broad groups: those acquired from official sources, those produced by commercial concerns and, thirdly, products of the amateur photographer. The last-named includes the fourth group: the important negatives made by people during service careers or by a member of a particular ship's company.

Those negatives received from the Admiralty form the greatest number, the total being twice that of the Perkins collection itself. These are the work of professional photographers in the main and tend to concentrate on dockyard or warship-building activity. The principal exception is the 3,500 negatives of merchant shipping made during World War II. These were commissioned for the purpose of ship-recognition training and were largely taken by amateur photographers both afloat and ashore, although some are the work of professionals and some are by the Royal Canadian Air Force. The vast majority of photographs taken for official purposes during the conflicts in which the Royal Navy has found itself involved during the twentieth century are, of course, with the Imperial War Museum in Lambeth, London. Access to the Imperial War Museum's collection is granted on similar terms to that of the National Maritime Museum's. The majority of the remaining negatives in the 'official' category described above are concerned with activities at Portsmouth Dockyard from the 1860s to the 1950s. There is also a large number of photographs which were formerly at HMS *Ganges* and which are the work of R. A. Fisk, official photographer at that training establishment for 37 years.

Several amateur collections of high quality, mostly comprising ship portraits, are listed here. Mention should be made, in particular, of those photographs taken by Desmond Wettern when naval correspondent of 'The Sunday Telegraph' and later 'The Daily Telegraph'. Wettern's privileged position gave him opportunities to take photographs denied to the ordinary amateur.

Likewise, those photographs taken by officers or ratings (usually the former) who, as amateurs, took their cameras to war with them, often concentrate on individual vessels and are valuable for their wealth of detail regarding the ship, her service and her complement. The best included in the collections listed in this Guide were taken during World War I. Those taken aboard HMS *Aurora* (1913) and HMS *Laforey* (1913) have already been mentioned (p.24). In addition, the photographs

taken by Commander the Viscount Curzon, whilst serving on board HMS *Queen Elizabeth* (1913), and those relating to Engineer Lt. W. G. Turner's service aboard the armed merchant cruisers *Orama* (1911) and *Orbita* (1915) deserve mention.

Wartime restrictions on photography limited the number of pictures by amateurs to come out of World War II and there are few in the collection at Greenwich. However, Dr P. Ransome-Wallis took his camera with him when he served as surgeon aboard the cruiser HMS *Dido* (1939). Together with a number of portraits of merchant ships in convoy, his work includes many fine photographs of British warships at sea during the conflict. Ransome-Wallis's photographs will be found in this Guide listed with the mercantile collections.

The battleship HMS *Malaya* under way on the Clyde between January and August 1943 while serving with the 2nd Battle Squadron of the Home Fleet.
Collection: Ransome-Wallis
NMM Neg. No. N31823

The Royal Navy battleship *Cornwallis* was launched on Wednesday, 17 July 1901 from the Blackwall shipyard of Thames Iron Works. She took many blocks with her as she rushed into the water, the hot weather being blamed for the speed of the ways.
Collection: Adams
NMM Neg. No. N18691

Merchant Ship Photographs

This section of the Guide, which presents those collections of negatives best described as depicting 'commercial' shipping, embraces images of an extremely broad variety of vessels and maritime activity. Listed here will be found references to collections which include photographs of merchant sailing ships from the mid-nineteenth century to the last big, deep-sea square-rigger, built in 1926; also merchant steamships during their evolution from the earliest small, paddle-driven coastal packets to the biggest ships of the 1980s.

Every sailing ship rig is depicted, from the brig and schooner, through three- and four-masted barques, to the only five-masted ship ever built and the one seven-masted schooner. All types of steam and motor-ship are represented from tug to tanker and from lifeboat to passenger liner. There are photographs of sailing trawlers and drifters, and of coastal ketches and sailing barges as well as ocean traders under sail, and all manner of small, powered vessel. Also included are collections which hold photographs of sail, steam and motor-driven yachts, and local trading and fishing craft from around the world, particularly dhow and junk types. There is also comprehensive coverage of British beach-boats and fishing craft.

The life and work of the merchant seaman afloat in both sailing vessels and steamships is well documented. Many photographs describe how the ships were sailed and worked, and the nature of seafaring in the nineteenth and twentieth

This is the River Tawe, at Swansea, at low tide. The photograph is from a calotype negative and dates from the mid-1840s. In the foreground are two early steam paddle tugs. Among the merchant sailing vessels will be ships of the Swansea copper-ore fleet.
Collection: Talbot NMM Neg. No. C2256

Lying at Gravesend in 1876, this is the steam auxiliary passenger liner *Somersetshire*, built on the Thames in 1867 for the Australian service. Her sailing rig would have been utilised whenever winds were favourable, steam power being used in times of calms and to help the ship maintain her schedule.
Collection: Gould NMM Neg. No. G1310

The topsail schooner *A M Fox*, built at Appledore in 1905 and registered at Plymouth. She is seen here at Dover, drying her sails. During World War I the *A M Fox* passed to the Italian flag and was renamed *Gerardo*.
Collection: Nautical Photo Agency NMM Neg. No. P83

centuries. Within these collections are photographs of marine casualties and cargo-handling, of sailmaking, splicing and all the skills, occupations and mysteries of the seaman's life.

By far the most important of the collections listed below is that formerly held by the Nautical Photo Agency (NPA). There can be no doubt that it is due to the NPA that a large number of fine photographs depicting very many aspects of man's use of the sea has survived. The Agency was founded in 1926 by Captain Fred C. Poyser and the marine journalist Frank Bowen. Captain Poyser always had an intense interest in the sea, particularly in sailing ships and, after training in the *Conway*, served his time in the three-masted barque *Inverness*, owned by George Milne & Company. From the beginning of his career Poyser began to take and accumulate negatives of sailing ships and it is said that after he had gone into steamships he was sometimes able to persuade his captains to alter course when a sailing vessel was sighted, in order that he might photograph her. He saw the value of the photograph in preserving the memory of the sailing merchantmen which were fast disappearing from the oceans by the time he came ashore, about the end of World War I.

Together, Fred Poyser and Frank Bowen conceived the idea of establishing a central collection of maritime photographs which would be of use to historians, collectors and the news media. The purpose was to run the archive as a photo agency: to encourage photographers to place their photographs with it, without necessarily relinquishing ownership, and to benefit from any fees accruing from use of their pictures. Thus, although not intended as a national collection of maritime photographs, the work of the NPA in forming a nautical archive predated the subsequent efforts of the Society for Nautical Research. Once the Agency had been established and announced, the great number of friends and acquaintances whom both Bowen and Poyser had throughout the world began to deposit their negatives with the enterprise, or give them to it in some cases. Gradually the NPA grew until it comprised tens of thousands of negatives. Many of these were originals but Fred Poyser was very active in making copy negatives from those photographs which he held only as prints, so broadening the collection and incorporating many nineteenth-century images in its scope. Captain Poyser ran the Agency until his death in 1960, at the age of 71, after which it was gradually wound down by his widow, Grace. Many negatives were returned to those who had contributed them but, in 1966, the remaining 20,000 or so images of sailing vessels and merchant steamships, together with

The Clan Line cargo liner *Clan MacBeth* was built in 1942 as the *Ocean Glory*. Renamed in 1948, she is seen manoeuvring in port at Swansea in January 1957 when bound out for Glasgow in ballast.
Collection: Harris NMM Neg. No. N53021

One of the many types of standard cargo ship developed in the 1960s and 1970s as replacements for the ageing Liberty ship, this is the Fortune-type bulk carrier *Ria Luna* (1975). She is seen here in the Strait of Malacca working cargo in September 1983.
Collection: Airfoto NMM Neg. No. P44237(CN)

photographs of related subjects, were presented by Mrs Poyser as a magnificent gift to the Museum. The latest photographs in the NPA collection were taken in the 1950s.

Among the substantial holdings of negatives bringing the representation of merchant shipping up to date are the Harris collection, of some 11,000 negatives taken at Swansea between 1945 and 1970, and the Airfoto collection of 6,000 negatives. The latter, which includes many colour negatives and transparencies, extends into the 1980s and includes photographs of the most modern types of merchant ship, all being taken from the air. After World War II, Dr P. Ransome-Wallis specialised in photographing passenger ships; the bulk of his collection covers ferries and short-sea vessels around the world in the period 1950 to 1983.

The core of the representation of small craft, predominantly British but including some European types, is the collection formed by H. Oliver Hill. This collection has been mentioned (p.19) and it is further described below. Suffice it to say here that within the Hill collection will be found photographs of most of the types of boat,

barge and fishing vessel to be seen around the coast of Britain during the last century and a half.

Whilst, naturally, the photographs of merchant ships predominantly depict those flying the British flag, the Historic Photographs Collection and its associated collecting policy have never been restricted to acquiring images solely of British tonnage. However, for a period during the late nineteenth century, British shipyards produced four out of every five merchant ships entering service throughout the world. Thus, although often working under a foreign flag, the majority of the world's merchant fleet originated in British shipyards.

Photographs of foreign-built vessels are also important to a collection such as that held at Greenwich, allowing the development of the British-built merchant ship to be compared and put into context with tonnage constructed overseas. By means of this comprehensive accumulation of ship portraits, the design, constructional features and cargo-handling techniques that were characteristic of British shipbuilding enterprise may be evaluated against the products of the world's shipyards.

Shipbuilding Photographs

It was inevitable that once new techniques of production were widely established in late-Industrial Revolutionary Britain, a small island nation with such unprecedented manufacturing capacity would find its home market inadequate. It was imperative that industry should export if it was to flourish and, as that growth took place, equally vital that adequate transport be available to import the raw materials on which industrial expansion depended. Shipbuilding was therefore a natural concern to British commercial and industrial enterprise and one to which the new technologies in iron and steam-power were quickly applied.

Many of the earliest builders of steamships, especially on the Thames, have left no visual record of their activities and, with the exception of the remarkable photographs included in Barry's 'Dockyard Economy & Naval Power' (1863), the same applies to the marine engine builders of the first half of the nineteenth century. It is disappointing that this is so; for as one author has pointed out, in the middle of the century the greatest panorama of shipyards existing anywhere in the world was visible from the Old Royal Observatory in Greenwich Park, now part of the Museum.

During the thirty years from 1850 to 1880 British steamship tonnage increased by 1,600%, a figure which indicates the dramatic growth in United Kingdom shipbuilding capacity. In the same period, the tonnage of steamships owned in the rest of the world grew by just 440% and the majority of these ships would have come from British yards. By 1880 over half the world's steamships flew the British flag.

The merchant sailing ship continued to develop and to achieve increasing efficiency as a carrier of

HMS *Dreadnought* was built at record speed at Portsmouth Dockyard in 1905–06. This view, looking aft along the armoured deck, was taken on 28 October 1905, just 26 days after the keel was laid.
Collection: Portsmouth Dockyard NMM Neg. No. G10006

bulk cargoes. Regrettably, there are relatively few photographs (almost none in the collection at Greenwich) of these last, big square-rigged cargo ships under construction, although sufficient detailed views of the ships themselves exist to explain the innovations which kept sail competitive with steam in some trades until the 1890s.

Between 1892 and 1894, at a time when photography was becoming a commonplace activity, British shipyards produced over 80% of the world's mercantile tonnage, emphasising the degree to which ships, necessary to Britain's own imports and exports, had themselves become an export of considerable importance. The development of overseas shipbuilding capacity naturally caused this percentage to fall – to around 60% by the end of the century – but in terms of output the peak of British shipbuilding had not been reached. In 1905, for the first time, more than a million tons of shipping was launched in one year and this figure was exceeded again in the following two years. In 1913, a peak year, British yards produced 1.2 million net tons of merchant ships, which still amounted to 58% of the world total. Of this figure all but 30,000 tons were steamships. In the same year 193,000 tons of naval tonnage was also launched in the United Kingdom.

The construction of major warships in Britain during the middle and later part of the nineteenth century was characterised by a succession of technical developments and a number of transitional designs greater, perhaps, than shown in the evolving merchantman. The photographic record of this progress, culminating in the design of the *Dreadnought* of 1906, is fascinating and again makes one wish that more photographs had survived.

The collection of photographs relating to British shipbuilding at the Museum is not extensive in scope but what does exist is of considerable interest. The core collection of negatives representing merchant shipbuilding is that which originated with William Denny &

Bros Ltd. Only about 2,000 in number, the surviving negatives are just a proportion of those taken in the yard between 1880 and 1963, the remainder having been lost at the firm's liquidation. Nevertheless, these negatives are an important documentary source from one of the foremost shipbuilders of the nineteenth and twentieth centuries. Luckily too, prints from many of the lost negatives are in the photograph albums received by the Museum from Denny's when the firm closed, along with their collection of ship plans.

William Denny was one of Britain's earliest builders of steamships. In 1818 the 90-ton steamship *Rob Roy* was launched from the yard at Dumbarton and entered service on the Glasgow to Belfast route with passengers and mails, making her the world's first seagoing steamer engaged on a regular service. Denny's later came to specialise in short-sea passenger ships, producing many well-known vessels for railway companies. In 1879 the *Rotomahana*, the first large vessel with a steel hull,

Above: The mould loft at John I Thornycroft's Woolston shipyard on 30 November 1932. The wooden templates are for use in the construction of the motor yacht *Trenora*, an 856 ton vessel completed in July 1933 for Dr E G Stanley.
Collection: Thornycroft NMM Neg. No. G7794

Facing page
Top: The Cunard liner *Aquitania* is seen here at John Brown's yard, Clydebank, nearing her launch on 21 April 1913. The ship completed only three round voyages to New York before war service between 1914 and 1918. Her trooping service from 1939 to 1945 made her the only large liner to serve in both world wars.
Collection: Bedford Lemere NMM Neg. No. G10690

Bottom: In 1933 the Forth ferries *Robert the Bruce* and *Queen Margaret* were constructed by William Denny & Bros Ltd, the former being all welded and the latter of riveted construction. Two welders are demonstrating their skills on 14 November 1933.
Collection: Denny NMM Neg. No. P35157

came from the yard and the following year Denny's built the Allan Line's *Buenos Ayrean*, the first steel hull on the North Atlantic.

The Thornycroft collection of nearly 8,000 negatives represents the output of another specialised shipbuilder but, as with the Denny collection, these mostly derive from the latter part of the company's existence. Thornycroft's specialisation was in fast craft, particularly naval ones, and the company introduced a number of novel designs of torpedo-boat and torpedo-boat destroyer. Many merchant ships, particularly small passenger liners, came from the Woolston yard while the two yards on the Thames produced smaller vessels. As with Denny's, marine engine building was also carried out.

The third major British shipbuilder represented in the collection is Charles Hill & Sons, of Bristol. While fewer than 100 negatives were received directly from the firm, more than 800 were received as a gift from a former employee at the shipyard, Mr H. Breton. This larger group covers the last years of shipbuilding activity at Bristol and includes many detailed photographs of shipyard processes and activities.

Warship building is depicted in a number of small collections listed in this Guide, for example the building of the *Royal Oak* (1892), but the major documentation is to be found in the negatives presented by the Admiralty and by Portsmouth

Dockyard. The latter collection includes the magnificent set of 15 x 12-in. glass negatives showing the *Dreadnought* (1906) under construction, while in the Admiralty donation there are more than 1,000 negatives of the building of the *Hampshire* (1961).

Wooden shipbuilding is, not surprisingly perhaps, poorly represented and confined mainly to photographs of smaller craft under construction. These are mostly to be found listed among the mercantile collections.

Eighteen merchant ships were completed in British shipyards in 1993. Britain's contribution to the world total that year, in terms of both vessel numbers and finished tonnage was a little over 1%. The period of British ascendancy in iron and steel shipbuilding, through supremacy, to decline in the face of overseas competition and changing patterns of trade, encompassed a century or so from about 1860. Early during that time, the value of photography as a medium of record had been recognised by some leading British shipbuilders. That more photographs of Victorian shipyard technology and activity have not survived is a matter of regret: those that have tell the story of an industry now on the verge of extinction in Britain.

Three vessels under construction in the Clydebank shipyard of John Brown & Co Ltd in September 1960. The passenger liner *Transvaal Castle* is beyond the guided missile destroyer HMS *Hampshire*, with the cargo liner *Clan MacNair*'s bottom plates in the foreground.
Collection: Admiralty
NMM Neg. No. N17544

Topographical Photographs

When compared with the large numbers of negatives which form the collections devoted to naval and merchant vessels, there are relatively few which are primarily topographical in subject matter. Ports, rivers, harbours and docks obviously feature in very many ship portraits and where the location is known the information will be recorded in the Museum's indexes. Generally, it has been thought most beneficial in these cases to record the name of the ship depicted as the main subject of a photograph and the place where the photograph was taken as the secondary subject. Requests for photographs of named ships are far and away the most numerous received by the Museum.

There are, nevertheless, a number of important collections of negatives which are essentially topographical in subject and which by virtue of their range and quality merit a separate accounting here. The most notable of these, and the collection which forms the basis of pictorial documentation of British maritime locations in the archive, is that which derives from the Frith establishment. This collection has already been mentioned (pp.29–30) and is described in some detail below. The photographs are of the highest professional quality and are without exception on whole-plate glass negatives. Rather surprisingly, perhaps, it was thought worthwhile by Frith's to photograph industrial locations as well as picturesque coastal views and watering places. Thus we find photographs of docks and working harbours amongst those of fashionable resorts and simple, endearing beach scenes.

The two most important groups of negatives which contribute to the coverage of coastal Britain have also been mentioned (see p.29). The MacFee negatives are especially distinguished by the high quality of the photographic technique and eye which produced them, and by the long period of time over which the collection was amassed. The photographs were taken during the first half of the twentieth century and look back over fifty years of

The Ramsden Dock, at Barrow-in-Furness on the north-west coast of England, is seen here on 7 November 1932. The ship nearest the camera is the German cargo steamer *Thetis* (1909), discharging a cargo of pit props into railway wagons.
Collection: London, Midland & Scottish Railway NMM Neg. No. G3727

45

61076. St Ives, Pilchard Boats.   FRITH

Above: The pilchard and the mackerel were the most important catches for the fishermen of Cornwall and in this photograph, dated c.1908, fishing luggers lie, dried out, at St Ives. The vessels are strongly built, to take the ground at each tide, and sharp-sterned to enable them to pack together more easily in the small east Cornish harbours.
Collection: Frith
NMM Neg. No. G3224

Left: Foochow-type trading junks at Shanghai in the late 1930s. Foochow traders voyaged throughout the China and Yellow Seas, and other eastern waters.
Collection: Waters
NMM Neg. No. P34376

Facing page: The small port of Whitstable, on the north Kent coast, crowded with shipping at the turn of the century. These small merchant sailing ships, most locally-owned, are typical of the little brigantines and schooners which carried much of British coastal trade into the twentieth century.
Collection: Passey
NMM Neg. No. P27684

change in living and working patterns on Britain's coast.

The Fox collection of 3,500 negatives is similar in character to that of Miss MacFee, covering much of the same period but concentrating more on the southern half of the British Isles. Among the photographs in these two collections in particular, will be found depictions of many of the types of small British fishing craft, lying in harbour, sometimes dried out at low tide and with their crews busy about their decks.

Much smaller groups, among which might be mentioned the 11 negatives of the Fraser collection and the 66 of the Eagar collection, concentrate on particular locations; in the former it is Bosham, in Chichester harbour, Sussex, and in the latter the Thames. The Eagar photographs are an exceptionally fine set taken for the most part between the two World Wars. The negatives show Eagar to have been a most accomplished amateur with a very good eye for a picture. Eagar obviously relished his photography and it is natural to wonder why, in the course of twenty years, he made so few photographs of the river with which he was closely connected; and why there are not more pictures from his camera showing an industrial Thames, now entirely altered and its way of life utterly vanished.

There are a good number of images of foreign locations within the overall collection but the record is sparse in comparison with photographs of the British Isles. No major holdings of overseas topographical views are included, although many foreign ports, harbours and docks appear as the backdrop to ship photographs, as already explained. This is, of course, especially so in the case of photographs of local trading craft of the world, such as may be found in the Vaughan, Villiers and Waters collections.

In common with each main subject area represented in the Museum's archive, prints from negatives of topographical subjects described here are arranged so that all photographs of a geographical location, irrespective of the collection in which they originated, will be found together. The prints are ordered according to location in a progression around the British coastline, then across the English Channel to embrace the seaboard of all nations. This consecutive sequence of ports, harbours and shipping places follows that adopted by Lloyd's 'Maritime Atlas' and in use in Lloyd's publications for more than two hundred years. The coastline is followed round the mainland of the world, continuity being broken at convenient points to include islands and to incorporate each continent.

A pleasant scene at Maldon photographed in about 1895. Fashion at this time dictated that clothing was substantial and heads had to be covered. The only bare flesh visible is hands and faces.
Collection: Frith NMM Neg. No. G4397

The Collections

The foredeck of the Castle liner *Carisbrook Castle* (1898) lying in the East India Dock Basin, London, on 4 June 1898. To the left are other ships of the Castle Line. From 1900 mail sailings to the Cape left from Southampton; in June of that year the *Carisbrook Castle* closed the service from London.
Collection: Adams NMM Neg. No. N19677

HOW TO USE THIS GUIDE – TERMINOLOGY

This section lists the majority of negative collections held by the Museum. The closer that a collection is to being fully catalogued and printed, the easier it will be to access.

Collection Number/Name

A Collection Number relates the classifications in the Indexes to a named collection. For instance for an entry in the index: '*Discovery II* 1929 [expedition ship], 51'; here '51' in the Vessel Names Index refers to the Collection Number of the Discovery Expedition Collection, not the page number. Refer to the Collection Name rather than the Collection Number if requesting information from the Museum.

Acquisition

How the collection was acquired.

Photographer

Name of photographer, if known.

Number of Negatives

How many negatives in the collection.

Print Status

Indicates how much of the collection has been printed up in positive form.

Other Material

Items in this collection in addition to negatives.

Access

This indicates the accessibility of the collection based on how fully sorted, catalogued or printed it is. Items within a partially catalogued collection will be less known than those in fully numbered and identified collections.

The Indexes

The indexes are linked to collections by means of the Collection Number. These indexes are only a representation and are by no means comprehensive. Please look to the start of each specific index for an explanation of some of the terminology used in each category.

The vessel on which this breezy scene was taken has not yet been identified. It is, no doubt, a paddle steamer of one of the railway companies and the passengers here are crossing the Channel to France. The photograph dates from c.1906.
Collection: Adams NMM Neg. No. N19891

1   Adams.

Acquisition	Gift of Mr B Cheese
Photographer	Mr Edgar Tarry Adams and Mr Francis Adams
Number of Negatives	1,421
Print Status	Printed
Access	Numbered

Taken by Edgar Tarry Adams (1852–1926) and his son Francis (born 1882), this collection depicts shipping on the River Thames, passing through the Downs, and beach scenes in the Deal area.

2   Admiralty (Ministry of Defence, Navy).

Acquisition	Transferred or donated from various Admiralty sources
Number of Negatives	Approximately 12,500
Print Status	Negatives only
Other Material	Photographic prints and photograph albums
Access	Partially catalogued

Admiralty archives have been regularly transferred to the Museum and the Historic Photographs Section has received well over 12,000 negatives from this source.

Nearly 3,500 negatives are of merchant ships in British waters or Canadian ports during World War II and approximately 2,500 copy negatives relate to the work of the Royal Navy, Fleet Air Arm and Allied Navies during the same conflict. The latter were used principally for publicity and propaganda purposes at the time. There are also many negatives depicting damage to ships from enemy action or marine causes.

A substantial part of the collection depicts British warships and auxiliaries of the wartime and post war era. These are shown either under construction or after refits and dockings. There are close detail views of underwater fittings, decks and interiors. A particularly fine set of over 1,000 negatives follows the construction of the guided missile destroyer *Hampshire* (1961) at the

The war-standard cargo steamship *Yoho Park* (1943) is seen here at Esquimalt in March 1944. She is bound for Auckland and Lyttelton with a deck cargo of timber. On the long booms against her aftermast can be seen her anti-torpedo net defence.
Collection: Admiralty NMM Neg. No. P24426

Clydebank yard of John Brown & Co Ltd, from keel laying in March 1959 through to commissioning in March 1963. A good number of these negatives show the internal arrangements of the ship on completion, over eight different deck levels.

The balance of this collection is made up of general views of British warships between the wars, captured German hydrofoils designed by Tietjens and Wankel, and the salvaged Japanese midget submarine *Ha 19* (c.1938) which was wrecked at Pearl Harbour in December 1941.

3   Airfoto.

Acquisition	Part purchased and part gift from Captain R A P Foxley
Photographer	Captain R A P Foxley
Number of Negatives	Approximately 6,000
Print Status	Printed
Other Material	Photographic prints and transparencies
Access	Partially catalogued

In 1964 Captain Foxley established the Malacca Straits Aerial Marine Photo Service. This service built up a reputation for exciting and excellent quality aerial photographs of merchant shipping in the Strait of Malacca and became well known as Airfoto Malacca. Captain Foxley used a Piper Tri-Pacer high wing aircraft and took his photographs, usually using three cameras, through the open door of the aircraft. The Museum started purchasing negatives from Captain Foxley in 1974 and continued to do so until 1989 when the company was wound up as a result of his death.

The ships he photographed were usually under way in the Strait of Malacca and varied from very small coasters and tugs to ULCC (Ultra Large Crude Carrier) tankers. Dry-cargo ships, many with substantial deck cargoes, and passenger/cargo liners are much in evidence. Most of the specialist types of vessels such as Liquefied Petroleum Gas and Liquefied Natural Gas tankers, livestock and car carriers, drill ships and drilling rigs, heavy lift and semi-submersible heavy-lift ships and offshore support vessels have been photographed. Some vessels are shown under tow after suffering damage from marine or war causes and some ships are depicted working cargo at offshore anchorages.

4   Anchor Line.

Acquisition	Museum copies from negatives lent by Mr C A Somerville
Number of Negatives	26
Print Status	Printed
Other Material	Photographic prints
Access	Numbered, Sorted, Identified

This collection covers the launching of the bow section of the gas tanker *Traquair* (1982) and the matching of the bow to the rest of the vessel in Inchgreen Dry Dock, Greenock. It also includes depictions of the LPG (Liquefied Petroleum Gas) tanks after delivery to the shipyard.

5   Badcock.

Acquisition	Presented by Mr J F C Badcock
Number of Negatives	24
Print Status	Negatives only
Other Material	Photographic prints and photograph albums
Access	Numbered

The collection shows three different Landing Craft, Tank and two RAF refuelling launches under construction at the yard of D Badcock (Marine) Ltd, Cubitt Town, London in 1941–42. In addition, there are a number of views of a Landing Craft, Mechanised built by the company, showing her upon completion in August 1941.

Above: Under way here in the Strait of Malacca, in ballast, is the Norwegian Ore/Bulk/Oil Carrier *Obo Duke*. Built at Vegesack, in Germany, in 1973 this 78,000 deadweight ton motorship has separate compartments for the carriage of oil or dry-bulk commodities, as necessary.
Collection: Airfoto
NMM Neg. No. P43640

Left: Joining the bow and stern sections of the liquefied gas carrier *Traquair* (1982) in Inchgreen Drydock, Greenock in 1981. Ailsa Shipbuilders built the forepart of the vessel at Troon; the afterpart was built at Port Glasgow by Ferguson Bros.
Collection: Anchor Line
NMM Neg. No. C7074/19

6   Baiss.

Acquisition	Gift of Mr J L Baiss
Photographer	Mr L A Baiss
Number of Negatives	55
Print Status	Printed
Other Material	Photographic prints and lantern slides
Access	Numbered

These negatives were taken by Surgeon Llewelleyn Arnold Baiss RN, whilst he was on the China Station in HMS *Woodcock* (1898), a river gunboat, between 1901 and 1903. They depict British warships, including the *Woodcock*, and local craft.

Top: HMS *Linnet,* a screw gunvessel of 1880, served on the China Station throughout her career. Her landing party are shown exercising at Hankow in 1892.
Collection: Ballard
NMM Neg. No. B8815

Middle: Patrolling the vast Yangtse river, HMS *Woodcock* epitomises the gunboat diplomacy of the British government in the first decade of the twentieth century. The *Woodcock* served from 1898 until 1927.
Collection: Baiss
NMM Neg. No. N24368

Bottom: Members of the crew of the sailing ship *Zealandia*, built in 1869, making sennit mats whilst on passage in 1899. The figure on the left has been identified as Williams, one of the apprentices among the crew.
Collection: Barrow
NMM Neg. No. P20124

7   Bakker.

Acquisition	Gift of Captain H G Bakker
Photographer	Captain H G Bakker
Number of Negatives	17
Print Status	Negatives only
Other Material	Photographic prints
Access	Numbered, Identified

A variety of vessels, typical of traffic on the Great Lakes in 1956, were photographed by Bakker whilst he was working as a deckhand on the *Lakeshell* (1940).

8   Ballard.

Acquisition	Museum copies from albums compiled by Admiral G A Ballard
Number of Negatives	49
Print Status	Printed
Other Material	Photographic prints and photograph albums
Access	Numbered

As well as photographs of Admiral G A Ballard there are negatives which cover the officers of HMS *Linnet* (1880) in 1892, the

Originally ordered by Imperial Russia, the icebreaker *Sviatogor* was completed on the River Tyne by Armstrong, Whitworth in 1917. This photograph shows her in Royal Naval service in North Russia during the 1918–19 ice season. Now named *Krasin* the vessel is still in existence.
Collection: Batchelor
NMM Neg. No. B9588

Independent French Squadron, 1893, and views inside Admiralty House, Vittoriosa, Malta taken in 1918.

9   Barrow.

Acquisition	Donated by Mr R Barrow
Number of Negatives	44
Print Status	Negatives only
Other Material	Photographic prints
Access	Fully catalogued

Mr Barrow served as an apprentice between 1899 and 1901 on board the Shaw Savill & Albion sailing ship *Zealandia* (1869). His negatives depict life on board and show various members of the crew at work.

10   Batchelor.

Acquisition	Museum copies from an album lent by Mr J Batchelor
Number of Negatives	18
Print Status	Printed
Other Material	Photographic prints
Access	Numbered

During March to May 1919 British merchant ships transporting supplies to Archangel in northern Russia had to be led through the White Sea ice by naval icebreakers. The icebreakers were manned by British, French or White Russian crews.

These negatives show five icebreakers at work; the British-manned *Sviatogor* (1915) and *Alexander* (1916), the French-manned *Olga* (1915) and *Mikula* (1916) and the White Russian-crewed *Kosma Minin* (1916). The cargo ships being assisted include the *Stephen* (1910), *War Grange* (1917), and *War Down* (1918). One image is of the cargo ship *War Helmet* (1917) sinking in the English Channel after being torpedoed on 19 April 1918.

Calcutta Docks in the 1950s, with crowds crossing the Kidderpore Bridge. In the background is the Ellerman cargo liner *City of Madras* (1945), a regular trader to Indian Ports.
Collection: Baxter   NMM Neg. No. N63495

11   Baxter.

Acquisition	Gift of Captain R R Baxter
Number of Negatives	94
Print Status	Negatives only
Access	Numbered

Captain Baxter is believed to have been an officer with Clan Line Steamers Ltd in the 1950s. The majority of this collection appears to have been taken while he was serving on the *Clan Chattan* (1944)

and the *Clan Lamont* (1939). Ports visited were Southampton, Durban, Calcutta, Cochin and Tuticorin. Some of the negatives show various types of Indian native craft. There are seven views of Hiroshima showing the extent of the devastation caused by the atom bomb explosion of 6 August 1945.

12   Bedford.

Acquisition	Copied from photographs purchased at Christie's
Photographer	Francis Bedford
Number of Negatives	7
Print Status	Printed
Other Material	Photographic prints.
Access	Numbered, Identified

A small topographical collection of negatives copied from prints depicting Torquay in the nineteenth century.

The Louis XVI Restaurant on board Cunard's *Aquitania* (1914). This elegant compartment served as the First Class dining saloon on board one of the most beautifully fitted of all passenger liners.
Collection: Bedford Lemere NMM Neg. No. G10892

13   Bedford Lemere.

Acquisition	Purchased from National Buildings Record
Photographer	Mr H Bedford Lemere
Number of Negatives	515
Print Status	Printed
Access	Numbered, Sorted, Identified

Bedford Lemere (1864–1944) was a professional photographer and this is part of his collection of negatives. It is particularly strong on passenger liner deck and interior views during the period c.1890–1920.

Among the many passenger liners there are famous vessels including the *Mauretania* (1907) which held the Blue Riband for twenty years, 1909–1929. 176 negatives relate to the *Aquitania* (1914) and there is one negative depicting a drawing of the First Class restaurant reception area of the *Titanic* (1912).

The vessel interiors depict cabins and saloons of a variety of classes.

There are also shots of galleys, libraries, music rooms, gymnasia, hairdressers' shops, laundries, lavatories, swimming pools and engine rooms.

This collection also includes shipyard scenes at the Clydebank yard of John Brown & Co Ltd in 1901 and 1913. There are depictions of stockyards, warehouses, sawmills, woodstores, machine works, foundries and smithies.

Above: The Nelson Line employed a large number of passenger and cargo vessels in their UK to River Plate service. This photograph was taken on the bridge of the *Highland Loch*, built in 1911. Nearest the camera is the ship's master, at the engine-room telegraph.
Collection: Bedford Lemere NMM Neg. No. G10640

Right: This spartan accommodation is the Third Class Dining space aboard the Cunard liner *Saxonia*, built in 1900. The *Saxonia* carried 164 First Class, 200 Second Class and 1,600 Third Class (mostly emigrant) passengers.
Collection: Bedford Lemere NMM Neg. No. G10543

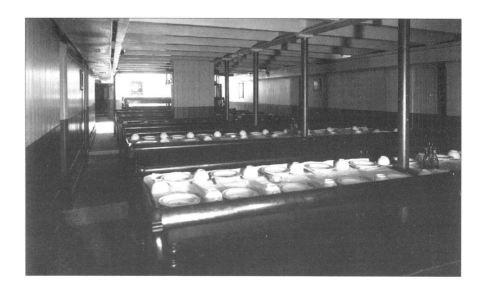

14 Bell.

Acquisition	Gift of Mr S Bell
Number of Negatives	18
Print Status	Negatives only
Other Material	Photographic prints
Access	Numbered

The Bell collection contains images of the 1937 Coronation Review, and yachts, Thames barges and passenger liners during the 1930s.

15 Bisson.

Acquisition	Donated by H W Bisson
Number of Negatives	14
Print Status	Printed
Access	Fully catalogued

The photographer took these negatives whilst in the Landing Ship Tank Mark II *LST 320* (1942) during the assault phase of Operation Husky, the invasion of Sicily. Some of the negatives show crew members and troops being addressed by officers during the approach to 'Bark South' beach, Cape Passero; others show nearby vessels. There are also scenes taken on the beach during the landing on 10 July 1943.

16 Boardman.

Acquisition	Museum copies from negatives lent by Mr M Boardman
Photographer	Mr C A Boardman
Number of Negatives	15
Print Status	Negatives only
Access	Fully catalogued

The J-Class yacht *Endeavour* (1934) is shown being towed by *Vita* (1931) on her transatlantic passage to the 1934 America's Cup Series. There are deck scenes on board the *Vita* showing, amongst others, Denny Drew and Gerald Penny playing deck quoits. There are also images of the *Endeavour* being rigged for the America's Cup Series by Frankie Murdock at Herreshoff's Yard, Bristol, Rhode Island.
The photographer, Mr C A Boardman, was assistant helmsman of the *Endeavour* in the America's

On 10 July 1943 allied forces invaded Sicily and here we see a DUKW amphibious lorry discharging from the US *LST 311* at Portopalo Bay in 'Bark South' sector. HM *LST 430* is in the background.
Collection: Bisson NMM Neg. No. N16956

Cup races of 1934. He also won a gold medal, which the Museum now holds, at the 1936 Olympic Games at Kiel when helmsman of the 6 metre yacht *Lalage* (1936).

17 Boyle.

Acquisition	Copied from photographs lent by Mr V C Boyle
Number of Negatives	26
Print Status	Printed
Access	Numbered, Identified

The majority of the negatives in this collection relate to harbours in North Devon, including the long defunct Hartland Quay. The date range is c.1875 to 1933. Clovelly, Westward Ho!, Bideford and Appledore are represented. There are also five negatives which show coastal sailing vessels in Italian waters, mainly at Venice.

18 Breton.

Acquisition	Gift of Mr H Breton
Photographer	Mr H Breton
Number of Negatives	857
Print Status	Partially printed
Access	Partially catalogued

Activities at Charles Hill & Co's shipyard in Bristol are shown between 1950 and 1977. These negatives depict the shipyard, equipment, dry-docks, the interiors of joiners' and pattern shops, vessels being built or under repair. In particular there is a long sequence of shots of the building of the *Miranda Guinness* (1976), a tanker for the carriage of Guinness stout.

The cableship *Anglia*, built at Barrow in 1898 and owned by the Telegraph Construction and Maintenance Co Ltd, is seen here giving a heavy roll to starboard whilst on passage at the beginning of the century.
Collection: Bromwich NMM Neg. No. C2127

Two shipwrights operating a pneumatic wood-boring drill in Bay 3 shed at the Bristol shipyard of Charles Hill & Sons Ltd in 1960.
Collection: Breton NMM Neg. No. P36544

19 Brixham Museum and History Society.

Acquisition	Museum copies from photographs lent by Brixham Museum and History Society
Number of Negatives	30
Print Status	Printed
Other Material	Photographic prints.
Access	Numbered, Sorted, Identified

Fishing vessels and port and harbour activity around the United Kingdom are depicted. The collection also contains copies of photographs of deck scenes and interior scenes on board the yacht *Island Home* (1871), which was owned at Greenwich by Lieutenant-Colonel Travers in 1900.

20 Bromwich.

Acquisition	Museum copies from a photograph album lent by Mr Bromwich
Number of Negatives	44
Print Status	Printed
Other Material	Photographic prints
Access	Numbered, Identified

The subject of this collection is cable ships and cable laying c.1890–1910.

21 Broom.

Acquisition	Donated by Miss Broom
Number of Negatives	20.
Print Status	Printed
Other Material	Photographic prints
Access	Fully catalogued

Views taken aboard the battleships *Dreadnought* (1906) and *Bellerophon* (1907) form part of this heterogeneous group of negatives. Ship views are complemented by a negative of the steam pinnace from the royal yacht *Victoria & Albert* (1899). The remainder of the negatives depict various groups of people; liberty men seen alongside Southend Pier, boys of Lambeth Brigade Cadets, the naval party which pulled the gun carriage at the funeral of King Edward VII and the

30 July 1970 was a black day for the men of the Royal Navy – the traditional tot of grog would be no more. In happier times we see the men of the battleship *Bellerophon* queuing in response to the pipe "Up spirits". Dated 1909.
Collection: Broom
NMM Neg. No. P39024

eight man crew of King's Watermen of the State Barge of King George V. All of these negatives were taken about 1909–10. There is also a negative of Earl Jellicoe taken about 1930.

22 Brown.

Acquisition	Donated by Mr David Brown
Number of Negatives	3
Print Status	Printed
Access	Fully catalogued

The battlecruiser HMS *Hood* is shown being fitted out at Clydebank on 9th January 1920.

23 Browne.

Acquisition:	Gift of Mr W Browne
Number of Negatives:	Approximately 2,300
Print Status:	Negatives only
Other Material:	Photographic prints, transparencies and postcards.

A wide range of ships in British and foreign ports are featured. The collection falls into a number of periods: pre-World War II; 1947– 58, 1967–68 and 1972–76. This collection depicts mainly merchant ships, including some merchant sailing ships between the wars.

24 Burness.

Acquisition	Museum copies from an album lent by Mr V Burness
Number of Negatives	22
Print Status	Printed
Other Material	Photographic prints
Access	Numbered, Identified

Various ships of the Erikson fleet are depicted, as well as people connected with the vessels. Gustaf Erikson owned a renowned fleet of mainly three- and four-masted barques, whose careers as cargo carriers were continued by Erikson into the 1920s and 1930s.

This collection features a number of the most famous ships of this fleet; *Herzogin Cecilie* of 1902 (considered by Erikson as his flagship), *L'Avenir* (1908), *Killoran* (1900) and the *Moshulu* (1904). There are also some miscellaneous negatives depicting HMS *Hermes* (1898) sinking in 1914; the wrecks of the steamship *Prestonian* (1901) in 1915 and of the lifeboat *Alexander Tulloch* (1912) in December 1914.

25 Byles.

Acquisition	Purchased from Mr Douglas H Byles
Number of Negatives	Approximately 1,650
Print Status	Negatives only
Other Material	Photographic prints and postcards.

Topographical views of coastal Britain are depicted. These negatives come from two well-known producers of picture postcards, Photochrom and Harvey Barton, and were taken in the 1950s and 1960s.

The negative of this photograph, showing Mars Hill, at Lynmouth in Devon, was produced as part of a series for printing picture postcards. The collection dates from the 1950s and 1960s.
Collection: Byles
NMM Neg. No. P39163

26 Central Office of Information.

Acquisition　Gift of the Central Office of Information

Number of Negatives　Approximately 500

Print Status　Negatives only

Other Material　Photographic prints and transparencies

Access　Partially catalogued

Subjects covered include warships, general cargo vessels, container ships, tankers, cable ships, fishing vessels, research vessels, submersibles, yachts, motor launches and preserved ships. The negatives date from the second half of the twentieth century.

27 Christie's I.

Acquisition　Purchased from Christie's

Number of Negatives　74

Print Status　Partially printed

Other Material　Photographic prints

Access　Partially catalogued

British warships and yachts in the period 1890–1937 are depicted. This collection includes HMS *Hood* (1918), HMS *Courageous* (1916), HMS *Dreadnought* (1906), HMS *Revenge* (1892) and many more.

28 Christie's II.

Acquisition　Purchased from Christie's

Number of Negatives　23

Print Status　Printed

Access　Partially catalogued

This collection dates from c.1900 and depicts commercial fishing in Folkestone and Ramsgate.

The steel, steam launch *Yum Yum*, built at Dartmouth in 1896 is seen in this photograph at anchor at Cowes.
Collection: Christie's (I)
NMM Neg. No. G10465

Fishermen sorting their catch at Folkestone, c.1900. Most of these men are wearing the long leather seaboots, common to their profession.
Collection: Christie's (II)
NMM Neg. No. P32701

HMS *Antrim* showing off her graceful lines in April 1975. In spite of being completed as late as July 1970, she has already undergone a major modification by the replacement of 'B' turret with four Exocet missile canisters.
Collection: Central Office of Information NMM Neg. No. N18253

29   Chubb.

Acquisition	Museum copies from material lent by Captain H J Chubb
Number of Negatives	49
Print Status	Printed
Other Material	Photographic prints and photograph albums.
Access	Numbered

The images feature the Irrawaddy Flotilla Company, which operated passenger and cargo steamers along the Irrawaddy River in Burma from 1865 to 1942.

The Company ran both cargo and passenger services regularly along the river between Rangoon and Bhamo with some seasonal alterations. It used various types of vessels, amongst which were ferry paddle steamers, towing steamers, sternwheel steamers, creek steamers and launches, and various other self-propelled and non-propelled craft.

In December 1941 Rangoon was bombed by the Japanese and effectively ceased to function. The British Government then decided on a 'scorched earth' policy and it was as a part of this that most of the Irrawaddy Flotilla Company's vessels were scuttled in 1942.

The original photographs were provided by Captain H J Chubb, who served with the Company between 1919 and 1930. Captain Chubb was also a co-author with C L D Duckworth of a book entitled 'The Irrawaddy Flotilla Company', which was published by the National Maritime Museum in 1973.

30   Church.

Acquisition	Gift of Mrs J Church
Number of Negatives	12
Print Status	Negatives only
Other Material	Photographic prints
Access	Numbered

The images relate to the career of Captain Vernon C Merry DSC RN, when he was on board the destroyer HMS *Opportune* (1942) in early 1947. The images are of *Opportune* and her sister-ship *Obedient* (1942).

The *Lanpya* ('pathfinder') was the launch of the Superintendent of Pilots on the Irrawaddy. The twin-screw steamer was built at the Dalla Dockyard, Rangoon, in 1915 and was sunk in 1942 on the Japanese advance into Burma.
Collection: Chubb NMM Neg. No. B610/32

The brig *Avance* ashore on the Yorkshire coast. This may be the vessel built at Risor, in Norway, in 1857.
Collection: Clifford NMM Neg. No. C9772/11

31   Clarke.

Acquisition	Copied from a photograph album lent by Mrs E Clarke
Number of Negatives	18
Print Status	Negatives only
Other Material	Photographic prints
Access	Numbered

Scenes of naval interest are featured, mainly pre-World War I. This collection also includes the sinking of HMS *Warrior* (1905) on 1 June 1916, after the Battle of Jutland.

32   Clifford.

Acquisition	Copied from photograph albums lent by Mr H Dalton Clifford
Number of Negatives	63
Print Status	Negatives only
Other Material	Photographic prints
Access	Numbered

Enderby's Wharf at East Greenwich, London, is represented in this collection, with activities and people at the cable works as well as a negative of the cable ship *Scotia* (1862). Other subjects include the Gibson family, Mr Clifford's family and shipbuilders in Hull for four generations.

Facing page

Above: Seen in this photograph, off the entrance to the Royal Docks, London, is the Panamanian Liberty ship *Glyfada* (1944), in tow of the Watkins tug *Ionia* (1960). The American-built Liberty ships were the most famous of the war-emergency standard ships built during World War II. On this occasion the *Glyfada* was on her way to the Royal Victoria Dock with a cargo of grain.
Collection: Cochran
NMM Neg. No. P39164

Below: A general view of Dockyard Creek, Malta, on 14 November 1912. On the right is the residence of the Admiral Superintendent of the dockyard and Fort St Angelo.
Collection: Cotton
NMM Neg. No. N49034

---

33   Cochran.

Acquisition	Purchased from Mr I R Cochran
Photographer	Mr I R Cochran
Number of Negatives	Approximately 1,200
Print Status	Printed
Access	Sorted

This collection contains about 1200 negatives depicting mostly merchant shipping between c.1960 and 1975. A large number of the negatives show ships passing Gravesend. Other locations visited by Cochran (Markets Correspondent of 'Lloyd's List') to photograph shipping include London (the river and enclosed docks), Southampton, Dover, Liverpool, the Manchester Ship Canal, Harwich and Cowes. On the continent he visited Amsterdam, Rotterdam and Dunkirk. There are some warships represented.

34   Cocks.

Acquisition	Museum copies from material lent by Mr H C Cocks
Number of Negatives	24
Print Status	Printed
Other Material	Photographic prints
Access	Numbered

This collection depicts Appledore in Devon.

35   Colbeck.

Acquisition	Purchased from C M Colbeck CBE FRAS AINA
Number of Negatives	Approximately 250
Print Status	Negatives only
Other Material	Photographic prints, a photograph album and lantern slides.

The images in this collection are from the National Antarctic Expedition 1901–04 which was supported by the Royal Geographical Society. The aim of the expedition was the scientific exploration of Victoria Land, in the New Zealand sector of the Antarctic. There are images of New Zealand, Tasmania and Antarctica along with the three vessels mentioned below.

The expedition was led by Robert Falcon Scott. He was promoted to captain on his return from this expedition. Scott commanded the RRS *Discovery* (1901), a purpose-built research vessel designed with a strengthened hull to withstand the pressures of being icebound. Captain William Colbeck commanded the *Morning* (1871), which, along with the *Southern Cross* (1886), accompanied *Discovery* on this expedition.

The expedition set off from the United Kingdom in August 1901 and left New Zealand in December. It returned to England in September 1904. During this time Scott made various sledging journeys. On one, accompanied by E H Shackleton and Dr E A Wilson, the party reached a new 'furthest south' record, a southern latitude of 82° 16′ 33″.

36   Cotton.

Acquisition	Gift of Mr W D S Cotton
Photographer	Sir William Berry RCNC
Number of Negatives	205
Print Status	Negatives only
Other Material	Photographic prints
Access	Numbered

Taken by Sir William Berry of the Royal Corps of Naval Constructors, while he was serving in Malta as Chief Constructor, 1907–12. The images consist of many scenes of Malta, Berry's house, family and himself. They are involved in a variety of activities from bathing to playing in the garden.

The 30-ton electric travelling crane at the North Eastern Railway Co's Tyne Dock, Newcastle-upon-Tyne. This large crane was built by the firm of Cowans, Sheldon, of Carlisle, in 1908.
Collection: Cowans, Sheldon   NMM Neg. No. C6060

The scene on board a *Royal Sovereign* class battleship in the early 1930s showing the crew exercising with the starboard after 4in. QF Mk V AA gun. Notice the lack of protective clothing and the use of cotton wool as ear defenders.
Collection: Cribb   NMM Neg. No. N22251

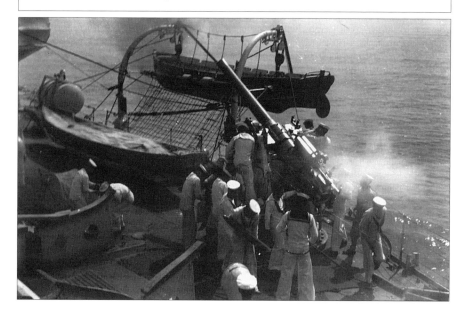

37   Cowans, Sheldon & Co.

Acquisition	Museum copies from photographs lent by Cowans, Sheldon & Co Ltd
Number of Negatives	9
Print Status	Printed
Other Material	Photographic prints
Access	Numbered, Identified

These negatives show dockside cranes and coal conveyors manufactured by the Carlisle firm Cowans, Sheldon & Co Ltd. They include both electric and steam powered cranes, constructed between 1908 and 1925, and operated at Tyne Dock, Sunderland and Goole.

38   Cribb.

Acquisition	Purchased from Mr G Pulham.
Photographer	Mr Stephen Cribb
Number of Negatives	511
Print Status	Printed
Access	Fully catalogued

Cribb was based in Portsmouth. The majority of the collection consists of portraits of British warships, ranging from battleships, aircraft carriers and cruisers down to MTBs, midget submarines and combined operations vessels. The launch dates vary from 1765 (HMS *Victory*) and 1871 to 1946.
Cribb also captured on film a number of events that took place in the area including the naval reviews of 1897, 1907, 1909, 1911 and 1914. He also photographed the arrival, at Portsmouth, of the President of France and of Crown Prince Hirohito of Japan in 1913 and 1921 respectively. Winston Churchill is photographed on four separate occasions between 1912 and 1914. Also depicted are infantry and tanks exercising with a Landing Craft, Assault and a Landing Ship, Tank, c.1940–42; Wrens engaged in boatwork at HMS *Vernon*, c.1939, and ratings working on naval aircraft, c.1937, and with a helicopter, c.1945. One of the few non-naval vessels is the yacht *Turbinia* (1894), the first vessel in the world to be powered by a steam turbine.

39   Crissup.

Acquisition	Gift of Mr C J Crissup.
Photographer	Possibly the work of E C Stevens
Number of Negatives	56
Print Status	Negatives only
Other Material	Photographic prints
Access	Fully catalogued

Some of these images were taken at the Albion shipyard of Charles Hill & Sons Ltd, Bristol. They depict vessels being launched and on the stocks. While most of the negatives are of c.1917–20, there are a number of copies of woodcuts from the 'Illustrated London News' depicting the *Great Eastern* (1858).

40   Crockett.

Acquisition	Copied from photographs donated by Major Kirkpatrick-Crockett
Photographer	Mr W M Crockett
Number of Negatives	68
Print Status	Printed
Other Material	Photographic prints
Access	Fully catalogued

This collection consists almost entirely of negatives of Royal Naval interest taken in the Plymouth and Devonport area. Most date from c.1900–14, many showing battleships and cruisers passing through the Narrows on their way to or from the dockyard. Others show the launch of the battleship *Hibernia* (1905) and the battlecruiser *Lion* (1910), and the submarine depot ship *Forth* (1886) moored in the Hamoaze with her attendant submarines. This collection also depicts the gates to the Royal Naval Barracks, Devonport, and the Royal Naval College, Dartmouth. A proportion of the collection is devoted to the training ships based in the area including *Impregnable* (1860), *Lion* (1847), *Circe* (1827) and the *Powerful* establishment. In addition, the *Ganges* training establishment at Shotley is depicted.

Charles Hill & Sons Ltd were shipbuilders, ship owners and managers based in Bristol. They managed the Bristol City Line of steamships and on 12 June 1920 the cargo ship Boston City was launched for the Line at Hill's own Albion shipyard.
Collection: Crissup
NMM Neg. No. N23298

The armoured broadside cruiser HMS Northampton laid to a buoy at Plymouth in 1886. She had just returned from a period of service as flagship of the North America and West Indies Station.
Collection: Crockett
NMM Neg. No. N29416

Commander the Viscount Curzon RNVR joined the battleship HMS *Queen Elizabeth* in December 1914 and served in her until early 1919. By 12 April 1916, when this photograph was taken, his cabin had acquired a permanent 'lived-in' look.
Collection: Curzon NMM Neg. No. N16648

The SD14 standard cargo ship *Santa Katerina* was completed by Austin & Pickersgill, who developed the type, at Sunderland in 1971. Of 14,000 deadweight tons, the SD14 was designed as a replacement for the famous Liberty ship of World War II.
Collection: Davies, D P B NMM Neg. No. P28171

41   Curzon.

Acquisition	Purchased from Onslow Auctions Ltd
Photographer	Commander the Viscount Curzon (later 5th Earl Howe) 1884–1964
Number of Negatives	399
Print Status	Printed
Access	Fully catalogued

Taken by Commander the Viscount Curzon between 1915 and 1917 when he served on HMS *Queen Elizabeth* (1913), these negatives depict the Grand Fleet and the various Battle Squadrons and units that it comprised. There are pictures of capital ships such as HMS *Barham* (1914), HMS *Iron Duke* (1912), and HMS *Collingwood* (1908). A variety of other ship types and classes are depicted.
A number of negatives show detailed views of HMS *Warspite* (1913) in dry dock at Rosyth, undergoing repairs to battle damage sustained on 31 May 1916 at the Battle of Jutland.
This collection also depicts life on board ship during World War I, including portraits of identified people of all ranks. There are pictures of decks and ship interiors on HMS *Queen Elizabeth* including officers' cabins and the Petty Officers' Sick Berth. On-board entertainment and sporting subjects include regattas, boxing contests and football teams. There are pictures of the Royal Marines Band on deck and the ship's Gunroom Concert Party, the cast in various costumes.

42   Davies, Captain E L.

Acquisition	Bequest of Captain E L Davies DSC, RNR
Number of Negatives	28
Print Status	Printed
Other Material	Photographic prints
Access	Partially catalogued

In 1926 the Duke of Westminster had a new steel-hulled yacht constructed by Cantieri Navali Orlando at Leghorn. Completed in April 1927, this was named *Flying Cloud* and replaced the Duke's 1918 *Flying Cloud*. Most of the furnishings, fittings and equipment of the 1918 vessel were transferred to the new one. The negatives in this collection show both vessels at various stages, as the original was stripped and the new vessel constructed and fitted out, up to its completion.

Taken at Leghorn on 14 February 1927 this photograph shows, on the left, the stripped hull of the Duke of Westminster's schooner yacht *Flying Cloud*, built in 1918. Equipment and fittings are being transferred to the new *Flying Cloud*, lying alongside.
Collection: Davies, E L
NMM Neg. No. P39789

43   Davies, D P B.

Acquisition	Purchased from Mr D P B Davies
Photographer	Mr D P B Davies
Number of Negatives	112
Print Status	Printed
Access	Fully catalogued

The subject of this collection is merchant shipping from the 1950s to 1980. Mr Davies's main location is Swansea but other locations identified are Rotterdam, Singapore, Cape Town and New Zealand. About half of the negatives show various types of tanker, including coastal tankers. Cargo liners, general cargo tramps, bulk carriers and coasters make up the balance with just a few passenger/cargo vessels included.

44 Day.

Acquisition	Presented via The Maritime Trust, acquired from Mr V W G Day
Number of Negatives	59
Print Status	Negatives only
Other Material	Photographic prints
Access	Numbered, Sorted, Identified

The majority of these negatives were taken during various sailing barge races on the Rivers Thames and Medway in the 1930s; these include the Medway Barge Race of 1937 and the Thames Sailing Matches of 1933 and 1937. The vessels themselves are mostly spritsail barges built along the Thames and Medway around the beginning of this century. Also depicted are the passenger liner *Queen Mary* (1936) and the wreck of the four-masted barque *Herzogin Cecilie* (1902), both taken in 1936.

45 Denny, William & Bros Ltd.

Acquisition	Gift of Mr D I Moor
Number of Negatives	2,093
Print Status	Negatives only
Other Material	Photograph albums
Access	Fully catalogued

Rescued by the donor in 1963, at the time of liquidation of the shipbuilding company William Denny & Brothers Ltd of Dumbarton, this collection depicts all aspects of the company's activities.

Denny's was an important British shipbuilding firm. The family began building ships in 1818 although the first time the name William Denny & Brothers was used was in 1849. The firm was progressive and innovative, for example in the use of steel and in tank-testing.

From about 1880 a systematic photographic record of all their ships was taken. The vessels were captured on the stocks, while being fitted out and on trials. Unfortunately the majority of the negatives were destroyed and this part of the collection is far from complete. The Museum does however still have the positive images in its Denny photograph albums.

Included in the negative collection are scenes around the shipyard, such as fitting out docks, machine and engine works, joiners' shops, stockyards and construction areas. There are also design models of vessels used as builder's models and in tank-testing.

The vessels depicted are various, from fishing, passenger, cargo and service vessels to fighting craft. These depictions show interiors and decks as well as the vessels under construction and on trials.

In 1936 William Denny & Brothers collaborated with the Blackburn Aircraft Company to construct a factory on the site of Denny's old barge park. Work started in February 1937 and the progress of the undertaking was photographed up to May 1939, by which time the factory was reconditioning Blackburn Shark II aircraft.

46 Devitt & Moore.

Acquisition	Museum copies from the NMM Manuscripts Section's Devitt & Moore Collection
Photographer	Mr J W Lindt, Melbourne
Number of Negatives	21
Print Status	Printed
Access	Numbered, Sorted, Identified

Taken from an album in the Devitt & Moore Collection, these negatives depict life at sea on the passenger liners *Austral* (1881), *Orient* (1879) and *Orizaba* (1886). There is also a view of the passenger liners *Valetta* (1883) and *Chimborazo* (1871) at the Railway Pier, Williamstown, c.1887.

Facing page:
Top: This was the scene at Southampton as the Cunard liner *Queen Mary* (1936) arrived at the end of one of her first Atlantic crossings in that year. Nine tugs are assisting the ship into the Ocean Terminal.
Collection: Day NMM Neg. No. N49685

Bottom: Taken from Dumbarton Rock early in 1934, this photograph shows the fitting-out basin of William Denny's shipyard. In the basin are the paddle ferries *Robert the Bruce* and *Queen Margaret*, the paddle excursion steamer *Caledonia* and the cross-channel turbine steamer *Princess Maud*.
Collection: Denny NMM Neg. No. G11368

Below: Taken at Aden, about 1887, this photograph shows the Pacific Steam Navigation Co's steamship *Orizaba* (1886) being coaled. In common with most small ports overseas at this time, the coal is being carried aboard by hand.
Collection: Devitt & Moore NMM Neg. No. C4880/21

Gunner William G Worsh of the destroyer HMS *Swallow* proudly showing off his latest comforts from home, a hand-knitted cardigan and balaclava, in late 1918.
Collection: Dick NMM Neg. No. N11727

Loading cattle aboard the Norwegian steamship *Fleurus* (1919) at Port Howard, Falkland Islands, between 1924 and 1927. The *Fleurus* acted as a supply vessel to a whaling fleet.
Collection: Discovery NMM Neg. No. N45718

47   Devonport Dockyard.

Acquisition	Commissioned acquisition from J H Miller, General Manager
Number of Negatives	27
Print Status	Printed
Other Material	Photographic prints
Access	Numbered

Taken at the Royal Naval Dockyard, Devonport, these negatives show various workshop machines that were to be disposed of in 1982.

48   Dew.

Acquisition	Gift of Mr James Dew
Number of Negatives	6
Print Status	Printed
Other Material	Photographic prints and a postcard
Access	Fully catalogued

Shipping at Burnham and Highbridge, Somerset, is the subject of this collection. The excursion paddle steamer *Heather Bell* (1871) and the excursion paddle steamer/passenger ferry *The Lady Mary* (1868) are shown berthed alongside Burnham Pier, the former in 1901 or 1902 and the latter in 1882–83. The cargo vessel *Julia* is featured on her maiden voyage in 1904, under way in the River Brue at Highbridge.

49   Dick.

Acquisition	Bequest of Commodore J M Dick CB, CBE, VRD, RNVR
Photographer	Commodore J M Dick and Commodore P H W Haig-Ferguson
Number of Negatives	124
Print Status	Printed
Other Material	Photographic prints and photograph albums
Access	Fully catalogued

Warships between 1900 and 1925 are depicted. The collection is principally of British warships, such as the *Marlborough* (1912), *K3* (1916), and *Vindictive* (1918) as well as the royal yacht *Victoria & Albert* (1899). There are also views of German vessels, including the battlecruisers *Von der Tann* (1909) and *Hindenburg* (1915) and the light cruiser *Dresden* (1917). A number of the negatives were taken by Commodore P H W Haig-Ferguson.

50   Dingley.

Acquisition	Donated by Mr L A Dingley
Number of Negatives	414
Print Status	Negatives only
Other Material	Photographic prints and photograph albums
Access	Numbered

Dating from around the early part of the twentieth century and amassed by Dr E A Dingley, this collection is extremely varied. As well as merchant sailing ships and steamships of many types, warships of Great Britain, France, Italy and Japan, tugs, sail and steam fishing vessels, yachts and steam yachts, a steam lifeboat, sail and steam pilot vessels and lightvessels are all represented, plus a number of lighthouses.
Locations range from the Channel

A ward of the Seamen's Hospital at the Royal Albert Dock, London, sometime after 1902. From the inscriptions above the beds it will be seen that several were sponsored; by the P & O in the case of the bed on the left, nearest the camera.
Collection: Dreadnought Seamen's Hospital NMM Neg. No. D3016A

Islands, Weymouth, Portland, Sharpness, Portsmouth and Hastings in the south, to Ireland, the Firth of Clyde and the Western Isles. In the last two areas, the photographer captured many of the local steamers. There are views of Cunard's *Lusitania* (1907) fitting out, and others showing her in the Clyde upon completion.

Crew's washing day aboard the British India Steam Navigation Co's steamship *Wangaratta* (1919). This photograph dates from the 1920s.
Collection: Duncan NMM Neg. No. P32815

---

51   Discovery Expeditions.

Acquisition	Purchased from Christie's
Number of Negatives	186
Print Status	Negatives only
Other Material	Photographic prints
Access	Numbered

These negatives were taken on expeditions to the Antarctic organised by the Discovery Committee. The Committee was set up in 1923 as a body responsible for research into the oceanic resources of the Antarctic. Part of this was to provide the whaling industry with a scientific basis for its culling. The depictions are mostly of two expeditions directed by Dr Neil Mackintosh OBE in the 1920s.
The earliest negatives are from the expedition of 1924–27 which used the ship *Fleurus* (1919). Whaling scenes from South Georgia feature prominently.
Also featured are the research ships *Discovery II* (1929) and *William Scoresby* (1926). There are scenes of icebergs, ice floes, penguins, seals, an albatross and a sea elephant. There are also scenes from South Africa, the Suez Canal and Rio de Janeiro.

52   Dreadnought Seamen's Hospital.

Acquisition	Donated by the Dreadnought Seamen's Hospital
Number of Negatives	7
Print Status	Printed
Other Material	Photographic prints
Access	Numbered, Sorted, Identified

The Dreadnought Seamen's Hospital was first established in a former warship of that name, moored off Greenwich, and was transferred ashore in 1870 to the former infirmary of the Royal Naval Hospital, Greenwich. Branches of the hospital were later opened at the Royal Albert Dock and Tilbury. The negatives depict two exteriors of the Dreadnought Hospital, probably dating from the 1880s, and the exterior and wards of the Seamen's Hospital, Royal Albert Dock.

53 Duncan.

Acquisition	Donated by Mr Alex Duncan
Number of Negatives	132
Print Status	Printed
Access	Numbered, Identified

Taken aboard the British-India liner *Wangaratta* (1919), the collection shows scenes on board and ashore just after World War I. It includes a number of other vessels, a variety of places from Canada, South Africa, New Zealand and Australia as well as scenes from the Clyde yards of Fairfield Shipbuilding & Engineering Company Ltd and William Beardmore & Company Ltd.
Scenes aboard the *Wangaratta* include individuals, the cadets, the crew, the football team, man overboard practice and washing day.

54 Dunning.

Acquisition	Donated by the Ancient Monuments & Historical Buildings Inspectorate
Number of Negatives	48
Print Status	Partially printed
Access	Numbered

Portsmouth and the Solent are featured in this collection which covers two periods of time. Some 34 negatives were taken around 1910 and show warships, merchant sailing ships, yachts and excursion paddle steamers. The remaining negatives were taken in the mid-1930s and show J-Class yachts racing and a two-masted schooner under sail.

55 Dunster.

Acquisition	Gift of Mr R E Dunster
Number of Negatives	23
Print Status	Printed
Access	Fully catalogued

The negatives depict sixteen warships prior to and during World War II. There are also several depictions of *Peking* (1911), a nitrate trader, at the time of her arrival in the Medway to be converted to a stationary training vessel renamed *Arethusa*.

Sir Thomas Lipton's yacht *Shamrock III*, built by William Denny at Dumbarton in 1903 and seen in this photograph under sail in the Solent. *Shamrock III* was the challenger for the America's Cup in 1903, losing to the American yacht *Reliance*.
Collection: Dunning
NMM Neg. No. P32467

56 Eagar.

Acquisition	Donated by Mr Waldo McGillycuddy Eagar CBE
Number of Negatives	66
Print Status	Printed
Other Material	Photographic prints
Access	Numbered, Sorted, Identified

W M Eagar CBE (1884–1966) was well known for his work with the blind and for the welfare of children, especially in the inter-war period. The negatives in this collection were taken at locations along the River Thames from Lambeth Bridge downstream to Woolwich, the earliest about 1914 and the latest in 1934. The scenes are of general interest rather than of specific ships and include views of Rotherhithe children cooling off in the river.

A rare photograph of the submarine *Umpire* taken off Chatham, where she had been built, in mid-1941. The *Umpire* was rammed by an anti-submarine trawler while straggling from convoy EC4 off The Wash on 19 July 1941. Sixteen of her crew were lost.
Collection: Dunster
NMM Neg. No. N23171

Foster's Wharf, in the Lower Pool, River Thames, during World War I. Beyond the Thames lighters in the foreground, the sailing barges are *Ena* (1906), *Success* (1903) and *General Jackson* (1896). There is also a Dutch barge, seen on the extreme right.
Collection: Eagar
NMM Neg. No. P27557

The Edwards family were Dock Keepers at the Falcon Dock, on the Thames at Southwark, in 1923 when this photograph was taken. In the background can be seen a number of Thames sailing barges, which were frequent users of the dock.
Collection: Eagar
NMM Neg. No. P27565

The Hamburg-South America Line's motorship *Monte Pascoal* (1931) was engaged extensively in cruising and in this photograph is seen leaving the moorings at Greenwich on the Thames, to which she was a regular visitor. In 1946 the burnt-out wreck of the ship was loaded with obsolete chemical munitions and sunk in the Skagerrak.
Collection: Elsden NMM Neg. No. N40620

J F (Curly) Edgell was a seaman serving in the Australian battlecruiser HMAS *Australia* in the period 1919–21. He is facing the camera and is seen maintaining a torpedo in the torpedo flat with another seaman.
Collection: Edgell NMM Neg. No. N17084

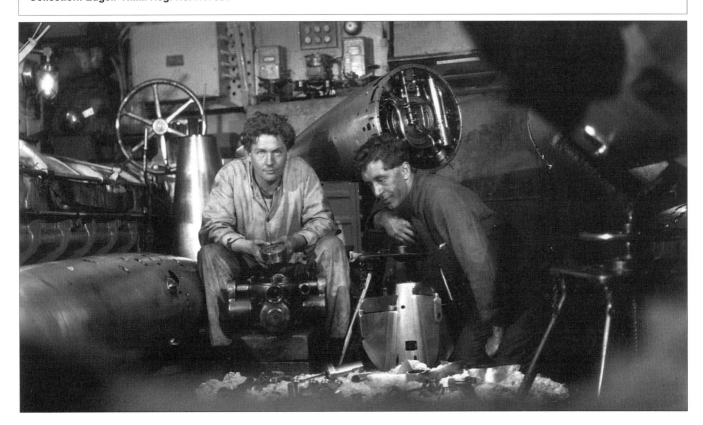

57 Edgell.

Acquisition	Gift of Mr James E Edgell
Photographer	Mr J F Edgell
Number of Negatives	65
Print Status	Printed
Other Material	Postcards
Access	Fully catalogued

Taken by Mr J F Edgell during World War I and immediately after, when he served on HMAS *Australia* (1911) and in submarines, this collection depicts life aboard the *Australia*, mainly in Australian waters.

58 Elsden.

Acquisition	Gift of Mr A Vincent Elsden
Number of Negatives	198
Print Status	Partially printed
Access	Partially catalogued

The earliest negatives in this collection were taken at Newhaven, probably before World War I. The great bulk, however, show merchant shipping, both sail, steam and motor, on the Thames in the 1930s. The photographer's favourite location was Greenwich Reach, capturing everything from passenger liners to tugs and spritsail barges. Of note are the Cunard A-Class ships of the 1920s, and the *Monte Pascoal* (1930) and *Monte Rosa* (1930) of the Hamburg-South America Line.

59 Everett.

Acquisition	Bequest of Mr Herbert (John) Everett
Photographer	Mr Herbert (John) Everett
Number of Negatives	77
Print Status	Negatives only
Access	Numbered, Identified

John Everett, the marine artist who made several voyages in merchant sailing ships and much of whose work is in the Museum, is seen here whilst taking passage in a steamship.
Collection: Everett
NMM Neg. No. N45671

The cargo liner *Kovno* (1907), seen here discharging timber in the Floating Harbour, Bristol on 17 December 1918, was one of the fleet of Ellerman's Wilson Line. She is painted in wartime camouflage and is fitted with a davit at the bow to handle paravanes as a defence against mines.
Collection: Fayle
NMM Neg. No. P29519

These negatives are the work of the marine artist John Everett (1876–1949) who was noted for his paintings and drawings of deck scenes on the ships he sailed in. His first voyage after leaving art school was in the ship *Iquique* (1892) in 1898–99, and the collection contains a number of on-board views from this time. He made a number of other voyages in deep-sea sailing ships between then and the late 1920s. He also voyaged in steamers in the 1930s. Everett painted in the Surrey Commercial Docks and among the ships he photographed there was the barquentine *Ferreira* (1869) (ex-*Cutty Sark*). There is also a portrait of Everett holding his sketch pad and pipe.

60 Fairburn.

Acquisition	Gift of Mr E T Fairburn
Number of Negatives	4
Print Status	Printed
Other Material	Photographic prints
Access	Fully catalogued

The mid nineteenth century naval vessels *Minotaur* (1863), *Lord Warden* (1865), *Hecla* (1878) and *Osborne* (1870) are depicted in this collection.

61 Falconer.

Acquisition	Gift of Mr John Falconer
Photographer	Mr John Falconer
Number of Negatives	195
Print Status	Partially printed
Other Material	Photographic prints
Access	Partially catalogued

A varied collection from an NMM staff member including depictions of the Museum's Tamar sailing barge, *Shamrock* (1899) at Cotehele Quay, Cornwall, in the late 1980s. There are also many modern photographs of Chatham and Burnmouth as well as images of the Merchant Navy Memorial and Samuel Plimsoll Memorial, London. In addition to this there are copy negatives showing the effects of the 1874 cyclone in Hong Kong.

62   Fayle.

Acquisition	Gift of Mr R L Tickett
Number of	
Negatives	1,719
Print Status	Negatives only
Other Material	Photographic prints
Access	Fully catalogued

This collection of ship images was the property of Brigadier L R E Fayle, CBE, DSO, ARINA (1903–72) and was presented to the Museum by his son-in-law. The collection spans half a century, from 1913 to 1967. The vessels are mercantile, British and foreign, and Brigadier Fayle concentrated his efforts on Avonmouth, Bristol, London and Southampton.

63   Fisher.

Acquisition	Gift of Mr J Fisher
Photographer	Mr J Fisher
Number of	
Negatives	17
Print Status	Partially printed
Other Material	Photographic prints and postcards
Access	Numbered, Identified

Taken in 1963, a number are of the passenger liner *Queen Mary* (1936) at Southampton. There are also depictions of the *Transvaal Castle* (1961), the Woolwich ferry, London, the River Thames at Westminster and one of HMS *Victory* (1765), Portsmouth.

64   Fisk.

Acquisition	Gift of Mr R A Fisk
Photographer	Mr R A Fisk
Number of	
Negatives	Approximately 40,000
Print Status	Negatives only
Other Material	Photographic prints
Access	Partially catalogued

Mr Fisk was the official photographer for the boys' training establishment HMS *Ganges* at Shotley, near Harwich, from 1939 until its closure in 1976. In that time he photographed every boy to pass through *Ganges*. The majority of images taken prior to 1967 have not survived.
The subject matter is the day to day life of the establishment, including drill, games, schooling, displays,

V.I.P. visits, boatwork, presentations, celebrations, etc. There are also depictions of British warships of the 1950s to 1970s.

65   Flintoft.

Acquisition	Gift of Mr F Flintoft
Number of	
Negatives	348
Print Status	Partially printed
Other Material	Photographic prints
Access	Numbered, Sorted, Identified

These negatives are mainly of mercantile vessels at or near Hull, with a few taken on the Mersey. The period these depictions cover is mainly the 1960s and early 1970s.

The training of boys for the Royal Navy has been associated with HMS *Ganges* from 1866. In 1906 *Ganges* moved ashore to Shotley and in 1956 the boys became juniors. Junior D. Lowe of Drake Dormitory is preparing kit for inspection in March 1967.
Collection: Fisk
NMM Neg. No. N62874

---

66   Ford.

Acquisition	Gift of Mr H Ford
Photographer	Mr H Ford
Number of	
Negatives	18
Print Status	Printed
Access	Fully catalogued

The images are of ships at Brixham, Dartmouth, Teignmouth and Avonmouth in 1934 and 1937. The vessels include troopships/ passenger liners, such as *Lancashire* (1917) and *Somersetshire* (1921), in addition to cargo vessels such as *Maria Clara* (1883) and *Cushendall* (1904).

67   Fourmy.

Acquisition	Gift of N Fourmy
Number of	
Negatives	35
Print Status	Negatives only
Access	Numbered, Identified

Four different Poole Harbour passenger launches are depicted, including *Dawn* and *Polly*, taken about 1970.

Appledore, on the north Devon coast, was the last British port to own wooden merchant sailing vessels. Local boys spent their lives, out of school, on the quay and foreshore. Here some lads, including members of the prominent Slade family, are occupied paying the bottom of a boat.
Collection: Fox NMM Neg. No. P24448

This is Bridlington, in Yorkshire, on a fine day shortly before World War I. In the harbour are a large number of cobles, the fishing craft characteristic of this coast, and at the mole is the paddle steamer *Scarborough* (1866) just returned from a pleasure trip.
Collection: Frith NMM Neg. No. G3291

68 Fox.

Acquisition	Gift of Mr W C Fox
Photographer	Mr S C Fox
Number of Negatives	3,560
Print Status	Partially printed
Other Material	Photographic prints
Access	Numbered

Scenes from around the coast of England and Wales are featured in this large topographical collection. In particular, places such as Appledore, Scarborough, Whitby, Ramsgate, Hastings, Looe, Polperro, Mevagissey, the Norfolk coast, the West Country and the Welsh coast are featured. The negatives date from the early part of the twentieth century.

69 Fraser.

Acquisition	Bequest of Mrs E M Fraser
Number of Negatives	11
Print Status	Printed
Access	Numbered, Identified

A small series of negatives taken at Bosham about 1904, showing sailing vessels alongside the quay and local fishermen with their boats and nets.

70 Frith.

Acquisition	Purchased from Francis Frith & Co
Photographer	Frith & Co
Number of Negatives	1,167
Print Status	Printed
Access	Numbered, Sorted, Identified

The firm of Frith & Co, founded by Francis Frith (1822–98), was renowned for its topographical postcards and became the largest photographic publishing company in the world. In 1971, when the firm went into liquidation, the Museum purchased many of the surviving glass negatives relating to maritime subjects around Britain between about 1880 and 1940.
The collection depicts ports and harbours, resorts, beaches, fishing boats and fishermen, lake, canal and river scenes of England and Wales, Northern Ireland (and Kingstown and Howth in Southern Ireland), the Isle of Man and the Channel Islands. It is the Museum's finest topographical collection. Apart from the numerous ships and craft which appear in the general views, the collection includes specific ship portraits, the most notable group showing many of the best-known liners using Liverpool around 1890. There are also views of some of the old training hulks, such as *Britannia* (1860) and *Impregnable* (1860). For a more complete introduction to the Francis Frith collection, 'A Victorian Maritime Album' by Basil Greenhill (Patrick Stephens, 1974) is recommended.

Only a very small portion of one of the Frith negatives has been printed to produce this portrait of a Sheringham boatman. The whole photograph is a group of five men with their lobster pots and was taken about 1906. This enlargement is testimony to the quality of the large glass negatives made by the Frith establishment.
Collection: Frith
NMM Neg. No. C3231

HMS *Bellerophon*, a central battery ironclad, survived until 1922 although her sea-going service ended in 1892. She is shown fitting out at Chatham in early 1866. The combined clipper/ram bow is very evident.
Collection: Gadsden NMM Neg. No. C5531/E

71   Frost.

Acquisition	Donated by J K T Frost
Number of	
Negatives	Approximately 50
Print Status	Negatives only
Other Material	Photographic prints
Access	Numbered

A collection of film negatives relating to coastal shipping in Teignmouth in the years 1936–39. The vessels are principally motor and steam coasters but there are a few small sailing vessels depicted. A small number of negatives are of shipping in the River Exe.

72   Gadsden.

Acquisition	Copied from photographs lent by Sir Peter Gadsden
Number of	
Negatives	16
Print Status	Printed
Other Material	Photographic prints.
Access	Numbered, Sorted, Identified

Scenes in and around Chatham Royal Naval Dockyard, Kent, in the early 1860s are the subject of this acquisition.

73   Galton.

Acquisition	Gift of Mrs J Galton
Photographer	Mr E A Russell Westwood
Number of	
Negatives	570
Print Status	Negatives only
Other Material	Photographic prints
Access	Sorted

Line fishing at Kinsale in 1950 and shark fishing from the *Fathomer* (1941) at Falmouth in 1965 and 1966 are depicted. A 1954 voyage in the Danish sail training ship *Danmark* (1932) is well represented. Other material includes the motor yacht *Jean* (1932) during a 1962 cruise and views relating to the River Thames above Richmond and the boatyard of Tough Bros at Teddington.

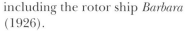
including the rotor ship *Barbara* (1926).

The remainder of the collection is principally concerned with British warships from 1863 to 1936. Various types of battleship from *Warrior* (1860) to *Rodney* (1925), a number of cruiser types of the 1890–1912 period as well as a number of destroyers are depicted.

Facing page:
This remarkable photograph dates from July 1932 and was taken from a house in West Ferry Road, Millwall, London. The Finnish barque *Penang* (1905) is in the Britannia Dry Dock, undergoing repairs. In December 1940 the *Penang* was torpedoed and lost with all hands.
Collection: Galton
NMM Neg. No. P39610

Above: The German battleship *Schwaben* was launched in 1901 and is seen soon after commissioning in 1904. She was disarmed in 1916 and broken up in 1921.
Collection: German
NMM Neg. No. N199

Below: The ship *Otago*, built in 1869 and owned by the Albion Shipping Company, at Gravesend on the Thames on 6 June 1874, shortly before leaving for Australia. She is drying her sails and on deck can be seen many of her emigrant passengers.
Collection: Gould
NMM Neg. No. G1780

74   German.

Acquisition	Transferred from the Admiralty
Number of Negatives	307
Print Status	Printed
Access	Fully catalogued

The origins of the collection are obscure. The negatives are all copies of photographs, half-tone illustrations, engravings, etc., and were 'liberated' from Germany at the end of World War II. Approximately half of the negatives depict German warships, taken in the period 1870–1939, with a particular emphasis on torpedo boats and submarines of World War I. The balance of the German warship negatives range from an armoured battleship of 1868 to a depot ship of 1937. There are a few depictions of German registered merchant ships and trawlers,

75   Goldsworthy.

Acquisition	Donated by Mrs Frieda Goldsworthy
Number of Negatives	40
Print Status	Printed
Other Material	Photographic prints and photograph albums
Access	Fully catalogued

Mr W T Goldsworthy was primarily interested in merchant sailing ships and their histories and compiled ten photograph albums containing a total of over one thousand photographs and a large number of ships' histories. In addition he had a small series of negatives which were taken at Scapa Flow in 1919. The majority show surrendered German warships at anchor but there are also views of the destruction of mine defences and three negatives depicting officers on board the store carrier and water tanker *Perthshire* (1893).

76   Gould.

Acquisition	Purchased from the executors of Mr F S Gould
Photographer	F C Gould & Son, Photographers
Number of Negatives	2,777
Print Status	Partially printed
Access	Partially catalogued

In 1855 the firm of F C Gould & Son, Photographers, was established in Gravesend. They photographed many of the larger vessels, especially the passenger carrying ships, which visited the Thames, catching them lying to moorings off Gravesend waiting for the tide. A small number of negatives were taken at Spithead in 1897 at the time of the Diamond

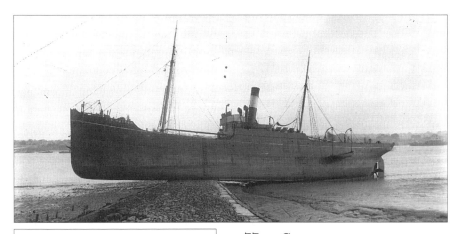

This photograph, of the steam coaster *T G Hutton* (1891) aground on the causeway at Tilbury, shows well the profile of a typical short-sea trading vessel of the late nineteenth century. The ship grounded on a falling tide but refloated safely on the next flood tide.
Collection: Gould
NMM Neg. No. G1472

Jubilee Review for Queen Victoria. Gould also photographed many of the spritsail barges which were a feature of the commercial life of the River Thames and also took many riverside views of Tilbury and Gravesend. The earliest dated photograph is from October 1871. With a few exceptions the remainder are between this date and 1914.

77   Gray.

Acquisition	Gift of Mr N G B Gray and some museum copies of photographs in an album lent by him
Photographer	Mr N G B Gray
Number of Negatives	237
Print Status	Partially printed
Other Material	Photographic prints
Access	Sorted

These images were taken by Mr N G B Gray while he was serving in the Royal Navy in the Mediterranean, 1940–42. In 1940–41 he was serving aboard HMS *Valiant* (1914) and in 1942 was attached to HMS *Mosquito*, the Coastal Forces base at Alexandria.

Depictions include HMS *Barham* (1914), HMS *Janus* (1938), HMS *Kimberley* (1939), and HMAS *Vendetta* (1917), all taken from aboard HMS *Valiant* during 1940–41.

78   Greenhill.

Acquisition	Gift of Dr B Greenhill
Number of Negatives	35
Print Status	Printed
Other Material	Photographic prints
Access	Numbered, Sorted, Identified

This varied collection is unified by their acquisition through Dr Greenhill, a former director of the National Maritime Museum and author of a large number of publications relating to merchant sailing ships.

Places depicted include Ilfracombe Harbour in 1870, Padstow Harbour, the River Mersey, Liverpool, Bridport in 1921, Appledore Quay in the 1870s and Australia.

Vessels depicted include a barge, a Brixham trawler, numerous ketches, schooners, sloops and the training ship HMS *Formidable* (1825).

79 Grierson.

Acquisition	Purchased and gift from Mr A R Grierson
Photographer	Mr A R Grierson
Number of Negatives	1,013
Print Status	Negatives only
Other Material	Photographic prints and transparencies
Access	Partially catalogued

Taken in the 1960s, this collection features a comprehensive variety of merchant shipping. Emphasis is on the London docks, at that time in their final heyday before containerisation. The collection, though primarily a record of the ships, also documents the working practices on the river at that time. Grierson was awarded the Winner's Shield in the World Ship Society, London and Home Counties Branch, Photographic Competition of 1964. He exhibited some of the winning photographs at the Port of London Authority Exhibition that year.
The collection also contains photographs, some in colour, of shipping in other British ports, notably Southampton and the South Coast ferry ports, and a sequence showing Sir Francis Chichester's return, in *Gipsy Moth IV* (1966), to Buckler's Hard after receiving his knighthood at Greenwich.

80 Guillaume.

Acquisition	Donated by Captain T D Manning
Number of Negatives	243
Print Status	Printed
Access	Fully catalogued

Although the negatives which form this collection are of poor quality, the subject matter is, in some cases, quite rare. The photographer was active from about 1902 to 1912, taking British warships mainly at Portsmouth and Plymouth. A number of those he photographed were laid up out of commission, some awaiting sale and some in reserve.
He also made at least one trip to

Belfast and Glasgow, where he photographed warships and merchant ships fitting out, and warships laid up in the Kyles of Bute. This trip appears to have been in 1906 or 1907. In 1906 he visited the Thames Ironworks shipyard at Blackwall and photographed some Rumanian river torpedo boats under construction. Three Japanese and two Spanish warships are depicted in addition to the wreck of HMS *Gladiator* (1896) off Yarmouth, Isle of Wight in 1908.

81 Gunn.

Acquisition	Donated by Captain P L Gunn DSM RN
Number of Negatives	406
Print Status	Printed
Access	Fully catalogued

Acquired through Captain Gunn of the Harwich Force Association, the identity of the photographer is not known, although the nature of the collection indicates that he must have been an officer serving on board HMS *Aurora* (1913) between 1915 and 1917.
The majority of the negatives depict HMS *Aurora*, the leader of the First Flotilla in the Harwich Force during 1914–15, and other vessels at Harwich in these two years. The *Aurora* is shown fitted as a minelayer in July 1917. She was also fitted with an aircraft platform for a Sopwith Schneider seaplane, which appears in some of the negatives, in 1915.

Above: This is the King George V Dock, London on 31 March 1962. At the quayside is Blue Star Line's refrigerated cargo ship *Ulster Star*, built in 1959 for the Australian service. The quay at which the ship is lying is now part of the site of the London City Airport.
Collection: Grierson
NMM Neg. No. P37352

Facing page, bottom: The destroyer *Janus*, launched in 1938, taking on bunker oil from the battleship HMS *Valiant* in the Mediterranean in 1940-41.
Collection: Gray
NMM Neg. No. D1094

Below: HM light cruiser *Aurora* was built at Devonport between 1912 and 1914, and served in the 5th Light Cruiser Squadron in the period 1915–18. She is here seen firing one of her starboard torpedo tubes in the North Sea on 27 September 1917.
Collection: Gunn
NMM Neg. No. N22751

Some of the vessels are shown badly damaged in warfare, including the Force's flagship HMS *Arethusa* (1913). Others are seen being loaded with mines at Grangemouth, as taken from HMS *Aurora*.
The rest of the collection includes deck scenes of the latter, including portraits of the officers and recreational activities on board.

82   Gunnersbury Museum.

Acquisition	Donated by Gunnersbury Museum
Number of Negatives	114
Print Status	Printed
Access	Fully catalogued

Taken at Scarborough in about 1912, many of these negatives depict seascapes, but there are a substantial number which show various types of fishing vessels in the harbour, drawn up on the beach, and working off the beach. These craft include Yorkshire cobles, Banff zulus and Scarborough trawlers. The lighthouse at the harbour entrance is prominent in a number of the negatives.

The Deperdussin tractor monoplane No. 1378 being taken to sea on board the light cruiser HMS *Aurora* in the early morning of 4 November 1915. The *Aurora* was a member of the Harwich Force at the time this photograph was taken.
Collection: Gunn
NMM Neg. No. N22556

Scarborough, on the Yorkshire coast. This photograph, taken c.1912, shows trading craft lying at the quay drying their sails and, on the left, women packing locally-caught herring into barrels.
Collection: Gunnersbury Museum
NMM Neg. No. P1143

83   Hamilton.

Acquisition	Donated by Mrs M Hamilton
Photographer	Commander Henry Hamilton
Number of Negatives	293
Print Status	Negatives only
Other Material	Photographic prints
Access	Numbered, Identified

These images relate to the naval career of Commander Henry Hamilton between 1910 and 1930. He joined the battleship *Superb* (1907) as a midshipman in 1910 and subsequently served in *Bellona* (1909), *Thunderer* (1911) and *Proserpine* (1896). While serving on *Collingwood* (1908) he was promoted to lieutenant and in December 1917 took command of *TB16* (1907). He spent long periods with the cruiser *Calypso* (1917) and the destroyer leader *Campbell* (1918) before joining the *Iron Duke* (1912) with the rank of lieutenant-commander. He commanded the gunboat *Cricket* (1915) on the Yangtse prior to his retirement from the service. The images in this collection relate to these vessels and to Commander Hamilton's service in the Mediterranean, Baltic and China.

Top: Built in 1910, the David MacBrayne paddle steamer *Mountaineer* is seen in this photograph under way at Oban during the 1930s. The *Mountaineer* was employed in MacBrayne's west coast of Scotland services.
Collection: Hamilton Ellis
NMM Neg. No. P38753

Middle: The *Polytimi Andreadis* (1943), seen here arriving at Swansea in 1956, was one of a class of more than 400 similar ships built in the USA during World War II. The T2s, as these tankers were designated, were powered by turbo-electric machinery.
Collection: Harris
NMM Neg. No. N57952

Bottom: The Royal Navy on patrol in 1907. The scout cruisers *Sapphire* and *Pathfinder*, both launched in 1904, maintaining station in an unpleasant swell.
Collection: Hedderwick
NMM Neg. No. N40503

In August 1914 Sir Ernest Shackleton left England in the *Endurance* on a voyage of discovery to the Antarctic. The *Endurance* became trapped in ice in the Weddell Sea and was crushed in 1915.
Collection: Henley NMM Neg. No. P11

84   Hamilton Ellis.

Acquisition	Purchased from Mr C Hamilton Ellis
Photographer	Mr C Hamilton Ellis
Number of Negatives	21
Print Status	Partially printed
Access	Partially catalogued

The vessels depicted were operating in the 1930s around the West Coast of Scotland, consisting mostly of paddle steamers owned by the firm David MacBrayne Ltd. There is also a wrecked trawler off Mallaig, paddle steamers on the Thames near Battersea Bridge, London, and depictions in Stockholm, Sweden, and on Lake Lucerne.

85   Harris.

Acquisition	Purchased from Mr R A Harris
Photographer	Mr Douglas D Harris
Number of Negatives	10,970
Print Status	Negatives only
Access	Numbered, Sorted, Identified

Mr Harris was the lock keeper at Swansea Docks and photographed the international shipping using the port between 1945 and 1970. Ship types range from small tugs and coasters to ocean-going cargo liners and tankers. A limited number of British and foreign warships are also included.

86   Hedderwick.

Acquisition	Gift of Mr S Hedderwick with some museum copies
Number of Negatives	25
Print Status	Negatives only
Other Material	Photographic prints
Access	Numbered

Taken between 1900 and 1914 these images include scenes at Portsmouth and in the Solent, scenes in an Indian port (possibly Calcutta), cruisers of the Royal Navy in rough weather, the passenger liner *Olympic* (1911) and the royal yacht *Alberta* (1907).

87   Henley.

Acquisition	Donated by Mr M Henley
Number of Negatives	48
Print Status	Printed
Access	Fully catalogued

These images relate to Shackleton's Antarctic Expedition of 1914 and the review of the fleet at Spithead by King Edward VII on 31 July 1909. There are also depictions of the training ship *Buzzard* (1887) at the Thames Embankment.

88   Hill, Charles.

Acquisition	Purchased from Charles Hill & Sons Ltd., Bristol
Number of Negatives	95
Print Status	Negatives only
Other Material	Photographic prints and photograph albums
Access	Fully catalogued

This collection was acquired in 1983 from the family of Charles Hill & Sons, the Bristol-based shipbuilders and shipowners. Much of the collection depicts the shipyard and vessels built by the company, the latter either being fitted out at Albion Wharf, Bristol, or under way on the River Avon.
A number of the negatives concern the warships built by the company between 1942 and 1946, including the River Class frigates *Tavy* (1943), *Trent* (1942), *Avon* (1943) and *Jed* (1942). The cargo vessels *Birmingham City* (1946) and *New York City* (1943) are shown being loaded at Avonmouth and a series of negatives depict cargo working at Avonmouth in the mid-1950s.

89   Hill, Henry Oliver.

Acquisition	Gift of Commander Henry Oliver Hill RN.
Photographer	Commander Henry Oliver Hill RN
Number of Negatives	Approximately 12,000 of which 4000 have been catalogued
Print Status	Partially printed
Other Material	Photographic prints and photograph albums
Access	Partially catalogued

This is the work of Commander Hill from 1914 onwards. He was an early member of the Society for Nautical Research, later becoming its Vice-President.
He lived in Newlyn and during this time was able to study schooners, ketches and various types of fishing vessels. He recorded details of the work of coastal seamen, and continued adding to his collection of negatives throughout his life. Those in this collection are mainly of small sailing and fishing vessels from the British Isles but there are also some pictures of fishing boats from northern France. Most of the negatives were taken in Cornwall but he also photographed vessels from all over Britain, such as Northumberland cobles, Manx nickies, Appledore skiffs, Hastings luggers, Brixham trawlers, baldies, bawleys, Falmouth pilot cutters, oyster dredgers, East Cornish luggers, Norfolk wherries, spritsail barges, etc. Other related subjects such as crab pot making, sail training and sailmaking are also shown.
Larger sailing vessels are also depicted in this collection, such as the three-masted schooner *Kathleen and May* (1900) and *Lawhill* (1892), a four-masted barque.
The fishing and sailing vessels are photographed underway, moored, at anchor, on trials and there are some depictions of their decks and interiors.
Some of the pictures are topographical views of various British coastal towns mainly in Cornwall and Devon but also the Isle of Man, Sussex and several other locations.

Seen here, arriving at Newlyn with a cargo of salt on 10 February 1925, is the Danish topsail schooner *Hans*, built in 1907.
Collection: H Oliver Hill
NMM Neg. No. P70871

The *Nellie Mary*, of 60 gross tons, seen here dried out at low tide at Appledore in Devon, was built in 1882 and is typical of the small trading ketch of her time. The photograph was taken about 1915.
Collection: Hodge
NMM Neg. No. P27255

90   Hodge.

Acquisition	Purchased from Mr J P Hodge
Number of Negatives	85
Print Status	Printed
Other Material	Photographic prints
Access	Numbered, Sorted, Identified

The images feature sailing vessels at Minehead, Appledore, Lowestoft, the Norfolk Broads and Oulton Broad in particular. There are also some negatives of miscellaneous vessels in the Thames Estuary. The dates range from c.1912 to c.1920 and the craft include Norfolk wherries, schooners, spritsail barges and fishing vessels.

91   Houlder.

Acquisition	Museum copies from photographs lent by Houlder Bros & Co Ltd
Number of Negatives	71
Print Status	Partially printed
Other Material	Photographic prints.
Access	Numbered

Houlder Brothers & Co Ltd, the London shipping company, traded from the 1860s. The collection encompasses ships of this line and related shipping scenes, from the mid-1890s to the 1920s.

92   Howden.

Acquisition	Donated by Mr and Mrs Howden
Photographer	Paymaster Commander Donald Horatio Nelson RN
Number of Negatives	70
Print Status	Negatives only
Other Material	Contact photographic prints
Access	Numbered

The images relate to the career of Paymaster Commander Nelson, who served on board HMS *Danae* (1918) from 1922 to 1924 including the world cruise of the Special Squadron in 1923 and 1924. The *Danae* visited twenty-eight ports in seventeen countries before returning home.

93   Hurst.

Acquisition	Museum copies from an album donated by Miss G M Hurst
Number of Negatives	55
Print Status	Printed
Other Material	Photographic prints and a photograph album
Access	Numbered, Identified

The images relate to the career of Engineer Commander H Knapman between 1884 and 1909. Depictions include HMS *Raleigh* (1873) (Knapman's first vessel) operating on the Cape of Good Hope and West Coast of Africa Station in 1887. He later served on board HMS *Severn* (1885) on the China Station 1891–94. The last vessel to be included in this collection is HMS *Kent* (1901), also on the China Station, the photographs being dated 1908.

94   Hutchinson.

Acquisition	Purchased from Mr S Hutchinson
Number of Negatives	14
Print Status	Partially printed
Other Material	Contact photographic prints
Access	Numbered

This collection mainly depicts cobles and paddle tugs in the Sunderland area. There are also some sailing vessels, including the schooner *Carmenta* (1879) alongside the John Blumer & Co. shipyard. The negatives are believed to date from before 1928.

Launched in 1885, the second-class cruiser HMS *Severn* served on the China Station from 1889 to 1894. The chaplain, the surgeon and the engineer are seen in the wardroom with letters from home in 1892.
Collection: Hurst
NMM Neg. No. C3924

A traction engine, destined for service in the South African war, being loaded aboard the Houlder Line steamship *Denton Grange* (1896) at Southampton on 5 December 1899.
Collection: Houlder
NMM Neg. No. 8997/I

The Australian battlecruiser HMAS *Australia* is towed forlornly out of Sydney on 12 April 1924 to be ceremoniously scuttled off Sydney Heads. HM cruiser *Delhi* (1918) is in the background.
Collection: Howden
NMM Neg. No. N18384

Above: The Admiralty Modified W Class represented the ultimate development of the World War I destroyer. The *Vansittart* is shown at William Beardmore's Dalmuir shipyard in mid-1919 during fitting out.
Collection: Jarrett
NMM Neg. No. N24363

Top left: North Dock, Sunderland, during the 1920s. In the background are ships under construction at Blumer's shipyard. At the quayside is the schooner *Carmenta*, built in Denmark in 1879 and, when this photograph was taken, registered at South Shields.
Collection: Hutchinson
NMM Neg. No. G4146

Middle left: In the background to this photograph is the famous casino at Trouville, in northern France. Before it in the yacht basin are the elegant steam yachts belonging to the casino's patrons. The photograph dates from about 1912.
Collection: Irvine
NMM Neg. No. N23480

Bottom left: The Bridge Street, New York, offices of the steamship agents Pim, Forwood & Kellock about the turn of the century. The company were agents for, among others, the Atlas Line of Mail Steamers which served the West Indies.
Collection: Kellock
NMM Neg. No. C4167

95   Ilfracombe Museum.

Acquisition	Museum copies from photographs lent by Ilfracombe Museum
Number of Negatives	36
Print Status	Printed
Other Material	Photographic prints
Access	Numbered, Sorted, Identified

Views of shipping on the North Devon coast in the period 1880–1920. Ilfracombe, Clovelly, Appledore, Woolacombe, Combe Martin and Lynmouth are featured in this collection.

96   Illustrated London News.

Acquisition	Copied from the 'Illustrated London News'
Number of Negatives	5,644
Print Status	Printed
Access	Numbered, Sorted, Identified

The majority of the maritime illustrations from the 'Illustrated London News' from 1842 to 1890 have been copied onto 35mm film. The subjects covered include naval engagements and punitive actions, warships, merchant sail and steamships, personalities, special events, exploration, etc. The illustrations are all engravings rather than photographic.

97   Irvine.

Acquisition	Donated by Mr Hugh Irvine
Number of Negatives	55
Print Status	Printed
Access	Partially catalogued

Taken in the period 1906–14, the subjects covered include steam yachts, racing yachts and other yachts at Trouville, France. There are a few negatives of Lowestoft, a number showing F Miller & Co's boatyard (presumably at Oulton Broad, Suffolk) and some warships.

Peter Karney at the wheel of the Finnish four-masted barque *Pommern* (1903), steering by the wind on a passage in the early 1930s.
Collection: Karney
NMM Neg. No. P38580

98   Jarrett.

Acquisition	Donated by Mr B Jarrett
Number of Negatives	6
Print Status	Printed
Access	Fully catalogued

The shipyard of William Beardmore & Co of Dalmuir, Clydebank, is depicted in 1919. Two vessels were being worked on at the time, the destroyer HMS *Vansittart* (1919), which was fitting out, and the passenger liner *Empress of France* (1913), which was being reconditioned.

99   Karney.

Acquisition	Donated by the Reverend G H P Karney
Photographer	Reverend G H P Karney
Number of Negatives	96
Print Status	Printed
Access	Fully catalogued

Reverend Karney served on board the *Pommern* (1903) between 1931 and 1932. During this time he photographed the barque and the day-to-day activities on board, which ranged from sailmaking and rigging to haircutting and hanging out the crew's washing.

The *Pommern*, a four-masted ex-German barque owned by Gustaf Erikson, was used on the Australia run during the 1930s. The depictions are from a voyage which ran from 29 February to 7 July 1932, leaving from Port Germein in South

The Insect Class river gunboat HMS *Bee* of 1915, at anchor in the Yangtse river in about 1926 while serving as the flagship of the Senior Naval Officer, Yangtse. The *Bee* was broken up at Shanghai in 1939.
Collection: Kemp NMM Neg. No. N23259

This photograph was taken at Havana, Cuba, c.1904. Coastal passenger and cargo steamers are lying at the piers. There is a complete absence of any dockside cranes or cargo-handling gear and the ships appear to have loaded and discharged their cargoes using their own derricks and the chaotic mass of mule-carts seen on the quay.
Collection: Knight NMM Neg. No. D309/7

Australia, and arriving at Cobh, Ireland. She unloaded her wheat cargo at Glasgow. The negatives were taken both at sea and in port, and most, if not all, of the crew members are featured. There are also some scenes of the *Pommern* in dry dock at Falmouth the previous autumn.

100 Kellock.

Acquisition	Museum copies from material lent by C W Kellock & Co, London
Number of Negatives	13
Print Status	Printed
Other Material	Photographic prints
Access	Numbered, Sorted, Identified

The collection includes photographs of the offices of Charles Kellock, New York, pictures of the firm's saleroom and offices in Liverpool and the office of Pim, Forwood and Kellock about the turn of the century.

101 Kemp.

Acquisition	Gift of Mr M C Kemp
Number of Negatives	47
Print Status	Printed
Access	Partially catalogued

The majority of negatives in the Kemp collection depict warships on the China Station, mostly on the Yangtse around Shanghai, in about 1926. There are also topographical views of China of which the exact locations are unknown.

102 Killin.

Acquisition	Gift of Mr A Killin
Number of Negatives	15
Print Status	Printed
Other Material	Contact photographic prints
Access	Fully catalogued

These were taken on board the Norwegian passenger liner *Braemar* (1952), the Danish train/car ferry *Dronning Ingrid* (1950) and the Swedish train/car ferry *Malmohus* (1945). They depict the public rooms of the *Braemar* and the

train/car decks of the two ferries. The photographs on board the ferries show the method by which the railcars were secured during passage and the different types of bow doors used.

103 Kimber.

Acquisition	Donated by Mr Derek B Kimber OBE
Number of Negatives	317
Print Status	Negatives only
Other Material	Contact photographic prints and 10 postcards
Access	Numbered, Sorted, Identified

The Kimber negatives principally relate to shipping activity at Avonmouth in the 1930s. The photographs show individual ships

Caulking seams on the Royal Research Ship *Research* at Philip & Sons' shipyard at Dartmouth. The RRS *Research* was launched on 18 April 1939 and, to ensure that the ship was as non-magnetic as possible, was constructed of wood and non-ferrous metals. World War II halted her completion and the unfinished vessel was broken up in 1952.
Collection: King
NMM Neg. No. N39513

and small groups of vessels throughout the port, with the emphasis on ocean-going vessels. Tankers and cargo liners are predominant with tramp ships well represented; there are very few shots of coasters, tugs and similar traffic. Avonmouth was the terminal port for a number of fruit ships and these vessels are also covered. A small quantity of negatives were taken at Le Havre in 1932.

The submarine *E 26* had a very short career in the Royal Navy. She was completed in January and sunk in July of 1916. This negative was taken between 25 March and 25 April at Harwich, alongside the depot ship *Maidstone*.
Collection: Laforey
NMM Neg. No. N24165

Thames sailing barges off Northfleet, on the River Thames, c.1898. The nearest barge is the *Sales*, built at Woolwich in 1854.
Collection: Lambert
NMM Neg. No. N16967

104   King.

Acquisition	Donated by Mr C W R King
Number of Negatives	257
Print Status	Partially printed
Other Material	Photographic prints and postcards.
Access	Partially catalogued

These images relate to Philip & Sons Ltd, the Dartmouth shipbuilders. Over half the collection refers to the construction of the Royal Research Ship *Research* between November 1937 and August 1939. She was launched in April 1939 but was never completed.

Part of the collection depicts steam tugs and launches built or repaired by the company and the remainder are of various types of machinery, including steam engines, boilers and pumps.

105   Knight.

Acquisition	Copied from photographs lent by Mr P B Knight
Number of Negatives	22
Print Status	Printed
Access	Numbered, Sorted, Identified

Havana is shown between 1868 and about 1905. This collection also includes the British warships *Ariadne* (1898), *Fantome* (1901) and *Retribution* (1891), which visited Havana in 1904.

106   Laforey.

Acquisition:	Transferred from the NMM Manuscripts Section
Photographer:	Possibly the work of Probationer Surgeon-Lieutenant W A Byrn
Number of Negatives:	230
Print Status:	Printed
Access:	Fully catalogued

Taken between 1915 and 1917 these negatives are believed to be the work of an officer serving on board HMS *Laforey* (1913), possibly W A Byrn the Probationer Surgeon-Lieutenant. The *Laforey* was a member of the famous Harwich Force of light cruisers and destroyers led by Commodore Reginald Tyrwhitt (1870–1951). Most of the negatives show British warships at Harwich, although there are also views taken at Felixstowe, Dover, Portsmouth and the Firth of Clyde. There are many vessels featured in the collection, but special reference is made to HMS *Laforey* and the Laforey Class destroyers. The flotilla is shown at Harwich, Dover, Dunkirk and at sea. D and E Class submarines are also to be seen at Harwich.

A considerable part of the collection depicts life on board HMS *Laforey*. The officers and crew are seen participating in tasks ranging from dismantling a salvaged aircraft to cutting the Commander's hair. There are also scenes of gunnery exercises and portraits of some of the officers, including Byrn himself.

Other negatives show HMS *Victory* (1765) at anchor in Portsmouth Harbour, some C Class airships and various types of aircraft.

107   Lambert.

Acquisition	Donated by Mr F J Lambert
Photographer	Mr F J Lambert
Number of Negatives	14
Print Status	Printed
Other Material	Photographic prints
Access	Fully catalogued

Probably all taken by F J Lambert of Leigh-on-Sea, they are mostly of barges on the Thames including some taken at Ramsgate, between about 1890 and 1904. The spritsail barge *Sales* (1854) may be seen under sail off Northfleet and an iron paddle tug is shown towing a Danish schooner into Littlehampton harbour. There are also negatives of two ship models.

Top: One of the more atmospheric, artistic photographs in the collection is this view of Portland Roads in 1910–11, with two members of the 1st Division of the Home Fleet silhouetted by the low sun. HMS *Vanguard* is nearest to the photographer.
Collection: Latcham
NMM Neg. No. N21644

Bottom: Taken at the fish market, Copenhagen, in 1912, this photograph is one of a series showing activity in this busy quarter of the city. Of note here are the three steam-powered passenger launches.
Collection: Leicester
NMM Neg. No. P28395

108   Latcham.

Acquisition	Purchased from Mrs A Latcham
Photographer	Seward and Kestin
Number of Negatives	2,000
Print Status	Printed
Other Material	Photographic prints and postcards
Access	Fully catalogued

Naval craft at Weymouth and Portland are shown between about 1895 and 1950. There are also images of mercantile vessels. The collection provides a record of naval activity in Weymouth and Portland Bays, especially in the inter-war period.

Over half of the negatives depict British battleships, battlecruisers, cruisers and destroyers. Warships of other nations account for some of the collection.

These negatives were originally the work of two Weymouth-based photographers, Seward and Kestin.

109   Leathley.

Acquisition	Gift of Mrs Leathley
Number of Negatives	3
Print Status	Printed
Other Material	Contact photographic prints
Access	Numbered, Sorted, Identified

The wreck of the cargo vessel *Mando* (1944) is shown. This vessel ran aground during fog on 21 January 1955 between Men-a-Vaur and Golden Ball in the Scilly Isles, while on a voyage from Hampton Roads to Ymuiden carrying coal.

110 Leicester.

Acquisition	Donated by Dr G Zarnecki, Courtauld Institute
Number of Negatives	254
Print Status	Printed
Access	Fully catalogued

These negatives were formerly the property of a resident of Leicester, and were passed to the Museum in 1959 by Dr G Zarnecki of the Courtauld Institute of Art, London. Approximately half of the collection was taken in Sweden between 1900 and 1934, with the emphasis on the route of the Gota Canal and featuring a number of lake and river passenger and cargo steamers. Gothenburg harbour, Stockholm and Trollhattan were particularly favourite locations for the photographer. Three other Baltic ports visited were Copenhagen, Helsingfors and St Petersburg, the last two in 1912.

The photographer cruised to the West Indies in 1911 in the *Magdalena* of 1889 and made negatives at the various ports of call as well as on board ship. He also cruised in the Mediterranean at various times between 1903 and 1927, visiting Malta, Italy, South France, Egypt and Morocco.

111 Linacre.

Acquisition	Museum copies from material lent by Mr J Linacre
Photographer	A Debenham of Ryde
Number of Negatives	27
Print Status	Printed
Access	Numbered

Bembridge on the Isle of Wight is depicted in about 1907. The collection principally shows sailing yachts belonging to members of the Bembridge Yacht Club at the turn of the century.

Top: The British cargo ship *Ocklinge* (1923) is seen here at Lowland Point, in Cornwall, on 16 July 1932 after grounding on 4 March while on passage from Bilbao to Port Talbot, via Falmouth, with a cargo of iron ore. The ship could not be refloated and became a wreck.
Collection: Love
NMM Neg. No. P31658

Bottom: Charlestown is a lively commercial harbour in South Cornwall, its principal trade being the export of china clay. In this 1950s view, the little Dutch motor coaster *Badzo* of 1939 is in port to load her cargo.
Collection: Love
NMM Neg. No. P30528

Facing page:
Top left: The Scurdie Ness lighthouse, at the entrance to Montrose harbour in the west of Scotland. The light-tower is 127 feet in height. This photograph was taken at the beginning of the century.
Collection: McLintock
NMM Neg. No. P28275

Top right: Under way on the Caledonian Canal, this is the paddle steamer *Gairlochy*, built in 1861. Employed for many years on the Glasgow, Rothesay and Kyles of Bute service, the *Gairlochy* was lost by fire on Christmas Eve 1919.
Collection: McLintock
NMM Neg. No. P28244

Centre: This photograph, taken c.1887, shows the River Tyne at Newcastle. The majority of the ships seen here, with the exception of the large square-rigger, were engaged in the domestic and short-sea coal trades.
Collection: MacRae
NMM Neg. No. C2075/I

Bottom: This is Carradale, in Kintyre on the west coast of Scotland, during August or September 1924. The wooden framework is to support fishing nets while they dry.
Collection: MacFee
NMM Neg. No. N30620

112 Love.

Acquisition	Purchased from the Southwood Bookshop Ltd., London
Number of Negatives	2,044
Print Status	Negatives only
Access	Numbered, Sorted, Identified

Compiled by Miss Marion Love, this collection covers the period 1930–65. Miss Love is known to have amassed a collection of images of over 3,000 different vessels and the Museum has acquired substantially less than half that number, some 1,350 being represented in these negatives. The location of the remainder is unknown.

These negatives were principally taken in ports in the south of England. Known locations are London, Southampton, Falmouth, Fowey and Charlestown, although a number of images were taken at Santa Cruz in Tenerife in the 1950s. The ships are both British and foreign and cover a wide range of types, with a particular emphasis on coasters. Cargo liners and general cargo vessels are much in evidence and there are a limited number of passenger and cargo/passenger liners.

113 Lowen.

Acquisition	Donated by Mr R L Lowen MBE
Number of Negatives	16
Print Status	Printed
Other Material	Photographic prints
Access	Numbered, Identified

Taken at Hamburg and Rotterdam in 1945, these images show war damage to the cities and port facilities.

The unique torpedo ram HMS *Polyphemus* was built by Chatham Dockyard during 1878–82. This view is looking aft from her forecastle while at sea in the Mediterranean in 1899. Note the 5-barrelled Nordenfelt guns on the bridge.
Collection: March
NMM Neg. No. P75007

---

114 Mace.

Acquisition	Donated by the Reverend Helen Mace
Photographer	Reverend A W V Mace
Number of Negatives	103
Print Status	Negatives only
Other Material	Photographic prints, postcards and a lantern slide
Access	Numbered, Identified

This collection relates to British merchant ships and ports from the 1920s to the 1960s. Places visited by the photographer include London, the River Mersey, Plymouth, Sidmouth, Portree, St Michael's Mount and the Grangemouth Dockyard Co Ltd. The merchant vessels depicted are mainly ferries.

115 MacFee.

Acquisition	Donated and bequeathed by Miss Katherine MacFee
Photographer	Miss Katherine MacFee
Number of Negatives	1,817
Print Status	Printed
Other Material	Photographic prints
Access	Fully catalogued

Taken by Katherine MacFee (1881–1952) while on holiday in Britain and occasionally on the continent during the period 1902–51, this is a collection of vessel and topographical images.

The former concentrate on types of fishing vessels but also include yachts, spritsail barges and tugs.

The fishing vessels include trawlers, drifters, fifies, crabbers, baldies, smacks and skiffs. Also featured is the naming ceremony and handing over of the lifeboat *James MacFee* (1928) to the Royal National Lifeboat Institution. The cost of the boat was defrayed from the legacy of Miss MacFee's uncle.

Fishing ports and fishing-related activities are particularly well represented in this collection. Scenes include cleaning and packing herring, preparing nets, drying nets, fishermen's cottages and fishmarkets.

Topographical images include bays, docks, quays, wharves, harbours, lighthouses and castles in numerous locations, in particular the west coast of Scotland.

116 McLintock.

Acquisition	Donated by Mr F R Ashdown
Photographer	Mr John McLintock
Number of Negatives	100
Print Status	Printed
Other Material	Transparencies
Access	Numbered, Identified

McLintock photographed many of the Clyde passenger and excursion steamers that were in service in the period 1900–10. Some of the Clyde lighthouses and merchant shipping in the river were also recorded.

The capsizing of the three-masted ship *Comte de Smet de Naeyer* (1904) in the James Watt Dock at Greenock during fitting out in 1904, is featured. A few of these negatives were taken at Saltash, Cornwall, and Salcombe, Devon.

117 McNarry.

Acquisition:	Donated by Mr Donald McNarry
Number of Negatives:	20
Print Status:	Printed
Access:	Fully catalogued

The battleship *Vanguard* (1944) is depicted at Portsmouth on 31 May and 4 August 1960. Most of the negatives were taken on the ship's deck

118 MacRae.

Acquisition	Museum copies from material donated by Captain J A MacRae
Photographer	Captain J A MacRae
Number of Negatives	157
Print Status	Partially printed
Other Material	Photographic prints
Access	Sorted

The demolition of the coaling staithes at Blyth and Dunston in 1974–75 and views of the coaling staithes at Seaham Harbour in the same period are depicted. There are also views of Newcastle-upon-Tyne in the late nineteenth century.

119 Major.

Acquisition	Donated by Mr J K Major
Number of Negatives	30
Print Status	Negatives only
Other Material	Lantern slides
Access	Numbered

Locations featured in this miscellaneous collection include Great Yarmouth, Whitstable, Oban, Maldon and the Bull Point Lighthouse, Devon. There are some passenger vessels depicted, including the *Duke of Devonshire* (1896), a paddle steamer and the Union Castle passenger liner *Saxon* (1900). A number of the negatives show salvage work on an unknown vessel.

120 Manley.

Acquisition	Donated by Mr V S Manley
Number of Negatives	13
Print Status	Printed
Other Material	Photographic prints
Access	Partially catalogued

This collection shows Portsmouth, Southampton and Cowes, and warships in the area, c.1902–04.

121 March.

Acquisition	Bequest of Mr Edgar James March ARINA
Photographer	Mr Edgar James March and Mr Cuthbert J Greene
Number of Negatives	665
Print Status	Negatives only
Other Material	Photographic prints and photograph albums
Access	Sorted

Edgar March was the author of a number of classic books on small sailing craft of the British Isles including 'Spritsail Barges of Thames and Medway ' (1948), 'Sailing Drifters' (1952), 'Sailing Trawlers' (1953), and 'Inshore Craft of Britain in the Days of Sail and Oar' (1970). A good proportion of the negatives in his collection are copies that were made for use in illustrating his books. Many more he took himself, mainly around the Thames estuary and the south and south-east coasts of England.

About seventy of the negatives are the work of Cuthbert J Greene and were taken in the period 1899–1905. Greene was an Assistant Engineer in the Royal Navy through 1899 to 1900 and took a number of photographs of his ship, the torpedo ram *Polyphemus* (1881), while in the Mediterranean.

122 Marine Society.

Acquisition	Donated by the Marine Society
Number of Negatives	3
Print Status	Negatives only
Other Material	Photographic prints
Access	Fully catalogued

Warspite (1893), one of the Marine Society's training ships is depicted.

Epitomising the elegance of First Class travel by sea in the inter-war period, this photograph was taken, about 1930, in the First-Class lounge of the Canadian-Pacific liner *Empress of France* (1913) when the vessel was serving on the Southampton to Quebec route.
Collection: Marsden NMM Neg. No. D5413/17

123 Marischal Murray.

Acquisition	Bequest of Mr Marischal Murray
Photographer	Mr Marischal Murray
Number of Negatives	642
Print Status	Printed
Other Material	Photographic prints
Access	Numbered, Identified

Marischal Murray (d.1963) was the author of 'Ships and South Africa', (1933), and 'Union-Castle Chronicle', (1953); his negative collection reflects these interests. Approximately half the collection depicts merchant ships, mainly in the Table Bay area, between World War I and just after World War II. Murray travelled widely and some of the negatives are taken on board various passenger vessels between 1914–18, 1935 and 1937. Topographical views show such differing places as South and East Africa, Calcutta, Cyprus and the Aegean, Venice, Portugal, Tenerife, Singapore and Lake Titicaca.

124 Marsden.

Acquisition:	Museum copies from photographs lent by Mr Michael Marsden
Number of Negatives:	40
Print Status:	Printed
Access:	Numbered, Identified

People (models), are depicted on board the passenger liners *Empress of France* (1913), *Empress of Australia* (1914) and a Canadian Pacific Duchess liner, all in about 1930. Some of the negatives are copied from lantern slides of passengers on the after deck of the *Empress of Australia*. The rest show Chinese junks, the River Thames, St Ives, and various other places.

Built by Vickers-Armstrong at Barrow in 1929, for the Orient Line's Australian service, the *Orontes* is seen here in a Norwegian fjord on one of her northern cruises. After wartime trooping service the *Orontes* resumed sailings to Australia in 1948 and was broken up in 1962.
Collection: Marischal Murray NMM Neg. No. N44817

125 Mead.

Acquisition	Donated by Mr Rupert Mead
Number of Negatives	31
Print Status	Negatives only
Access	Numbered

These images relate to two voyages undertaken by the photographer. One was aboard the Houlder Line cargo vessel *Kingsbury* (1944) from Newport, Gwent, to Buenos Aires and the other was to Mombasa via Suez, possibly on board the cargo vessel *Empire Glory* (1943). The negatives were taken between 1947 and 1952. There are also two views of the River Arun at Littlehampton.

126 Medway.

Acquisition	Gift of Captain Noakes
Photographer	Captain Noakes
Number of Negatives	58
Print Status	Negatives only
Other Material	Photographic prints
Access	Fully catalogued

Captain Noakes was the nautical instructor on board Devitt and Moore's four-masted barque *Medway* (1902) in 1912. He was responsible for teaching the ship's cadets seamanship and navigation. There are details of the vessel herself and portraits of Captain Noakes and his family. Activities on board include various aspects of

A heavy sea breaking over the starboard rail of the Devitt & Moore four-masted barque *Medway* (1902) in 1912. A life-line has been rigged to assist the crew in moving about the deck.
Collection: Medway
NMM Neg. No. P8237

The upper reaches of the River Tamar, near Gunnislake. Under way on the river is a small paddle steamer carrying trippers and in the background can be seen Weirhead Lock which enclosed a cut serving the Bealeswood brickworks, hidden in the trees.
Collection: Merry NMM Neg. No. C2971

boat drill, hauling a shark on board, a fancy dress parade, deck games and a shantyman playing the violin. The barque is also shown in dry dock that year, her hull being repainted.

127 Melotte.

Acquisition:	Donated by Mrs R Melotte
Photographer:	Mr P J Mellotte
Number of Negatives:	42
Print Status:	Negatives only
Other Material:	Photographic prints
Access:	Numbered

The Royal Naval College, Greenwich, London, is the main subject of this collection, particularly views of the chapel. Also depicted are the Royal Observatory and the Royal Hospital School when it occupied what are now the NMM buildings.

128 Mennell.

Acquisition	Donated by Mr J B Mennell
Number of Negatives	31
Print Status	Negatives only
Other Material	Photographic prints
Access	Sorted

Southampton in the 1930s is the prime subject here.
The photographer has concentrated on the passenger liners which used the port but there is a small number of negatives showing other types of shipping, such as ferries and general cargo carriers.

The steel topsail schooner *C & F Nurse*, built at Falmouth in 1900, lying at St Mawes on 28 February 1925, having recently arrived from Garston.
Collection: Mennell
NMM Neg. No. N63724

The Round Tower at the entrance to Portsmouth Harbour is a popular vantage point from which to photograph shipping. The assault ship HMS *Intrepid* (1964) was captured by the camera of Mr D J Mills while bound out on 29 June 1970.
Collection: Mills
NMM Neg. No. N17209

129 Merry.

Acquisition	Museum copies from material lent by Mr I D Merry
Photographer	Mr I D Merry
Number of Negatives	49
Print Status	Printed
Other Material	Photographic prints
Access	Numbered, Sorted, Identified

Part of this collection is a record of a voyage undertaken by Mr Merry in the barquentine *Frances and Jane* (1878) in 1930. Many of these images have been reproduced in 'The Westcotts and their Times' [Monograph No. 25]. Other depictions are of the Westcott and Banks families and of Calstock and the River Tamar.

130 Mersey Docks & Harbour Board.

Acquisition	Museum copies from photographs lent by the Mersey Docks & Harbour Board
Number of Negatives	19
Print Status	Printed
Other Material	Photographic prints
Access	Numbered, Identified

This collection depicts Liverpool Docks, 1885–1905, and various types of dockside cranes and coal hoists. Dockside equipment of this kind is also shown in use at Birkenhead, Cardiff and at Port Richmond, New Jersey, USA.

In September 1917, while approaching Bombay with Turkish prisoners-of-war, the steamship *Edavana* (1911) caught fire. No lives were lost and although the vessel was badly damaged, as can be seen in this photograph, her engines and boilers were untouched by the fire. The *Edavana* was repaired and re-entered service in January 1920.
Collection: Mirrington NMM Neg. No. C7904/J

131   Merwe, van der.

Acquisition	Gift of and copied from photographs lent by Dr P van der Merwe
Photographer	Dr P van der Merwe
Number of Negatives	88
Print Status	Partially printed
Other Material	Photographic prints and transparencies
Access:	Numbered

These negatives, taken by an NMM staff member over several years, cover a variety of subjects including the start of the 1982 Tall Ships Race at Falmouth, HMS *Victory* (1765) under repair in 1977 and the *Amerigo Vespucci* (1930) at Greenwich in about 1977.

132   Mills.

Acquisition	Donated by Mr D J Mills
Photographer	Mr D J Mills
Number of Negatives	222
Print Status	Negatives only
Other Material	Transparencies
Access	Fully catalogued

This collection consists of photographs of liners at Southampton in May 1961 and warships at Portsmouth between 1961 and 1972.

133   Mirrington.

Acquisition	Museum copies from an album lent by Mrs B R Mirrington
Number of Negatives	16
Print Status	Printed
Other Material	Photographic prints
Access	Numbered, Sorted, Identified

Most of the negatives show the hired transport vessel *Edavana* (1911), after she was burnt out near Bombay in 1917. This collection also depicts the hospital ships *Madras* (1914), *Nevasa* (1913) and *Ellora* (1911). These four vessels were all owned by the British India Steam Navigation Co Ltd and were some of the large number which were taken up by the government as troop transports or hospital ships during World War I.
The album from which the negatives were taken belonged to Frank Maurice Thomas Jones, who was serving as an engineer with the company during the conflict.

134   Moffat.

Acquisition	Donated by H W Moffat
Photographer	Mr Moffat
Number of Negatives	44
Print Status	Negatives only
Other Material	Photographic prints and postcards
Access	Numbered

During the period 1935–39, the photographer, Mr Moffat (d.1958), made a number of voyages between Ipswich and London in the spritsail barges *Kimberley* (1900) and *Dannebrog* (1901), and one trip in the *Linwood* (1932) from Ipswich to the Tyne and Blyth. Other negatives were taken after World War II, mostly on the River Orwell.

135   Moore's Auction Rooms.

Acquisition	Purchased from Thomas Moore Auctions Ltd, Greenwich
Number of Negatives	24
Print Status	Printed
Access	Numbered, Sorted, Identified

Views of the Royal Observatory, Greenwich, c.1910 are shown in this collection. The remaining negatives show a number of unidentified people, and the exterior and interior of Rochester Cathedral.

136 Morgan.

Acquisition	Gift of Mr C Morgan
Number of Negatives	18
Print Status	Negatives only
Access	Numbered, Identified

This collection mainly relates to shipping around the south and east coasts of England, c.1910–14. A high proportion are either of, or were taken from, excursion paddle steamers.

137 Mortimer.

Acquisition	Purchased from Mrs F J Mortimer
Photographer	Mr F J Mortimer
Number of Negatives	2,500
Print Status	Partially printed
Other Material	Photographic prints
Access	Numbered

Mr Francis James Mortimer (1875–1944) was born at Portsmouth. He was a leading British photographer, winning more than 400 medals and awards. He was president of the Royal Photographic Society, 1940–42, and editor of a number of photographic journals.

The examples of his work purchased by the Museum date from c.1900 to the 1930s and have a strong Portsmouth and Solent bias. As well as many warship views, he has provided us with some excellent coverage of the Camber, Portsmouth, and some fine photographs of the Royal Naval Barracks in Queen Street.

Events covered by Mortimer include the last journey of Queen Victoria, 1 February 1901, the departure of the Duke and Duchess of York (the future King George V and Queen Mary) for a tour of the Empire in the *Ophir* (1891), March 1901, the visit of the U.S. Navy Squadron to Portsmouth, July 1903, and the Spithead Reviews of 1911, 1935 and 1937.

Most of the Museum's yachting negatives are by Mortimer, the majority showing racing in the Solent. However, a number are of yacht racing in Sydney Harbour.

On 16 July 1935 His Majesty King George V reviewed the Fleet at Spithead. The following day he led it to sea for exercises and here we see the battleship *Valiant* astern of her sister *Barham,* in mid-morning at tot time.
Collection: Mortimer
NMM Neg. No. P60657

On-board views of the White Star Line passenger liners *Britannic* (1930) and *Georgic* (1932) were probably taken in 1933.

Places depicted include the Isles of Scilly, Bosham and Selsey, Sussex, Harland and Wolff's Yard, Belfast, c.1924, Porthleven, Cornwall, the Norfolk Broads and Blankenberghe, Belgium.

138 Moulson.

Acquisition	Museum copies from material lent by Commander J A C Moulson
Number of Negatives	10
Print Status	Printed
Access	Numbered, Sorted, Identified

The pirating of the China Navigation Co's passenger/cargo vessel *Shuntien* (1934) in June 1934 is the subject of this collection. It includes aerial views of the pirates' lair, views taken on board HMS *Eagle* (1918), and of her aircraft, which played a major part in rescuing the Britons taken captive. There are no photographs of the *Shuntien* herself.

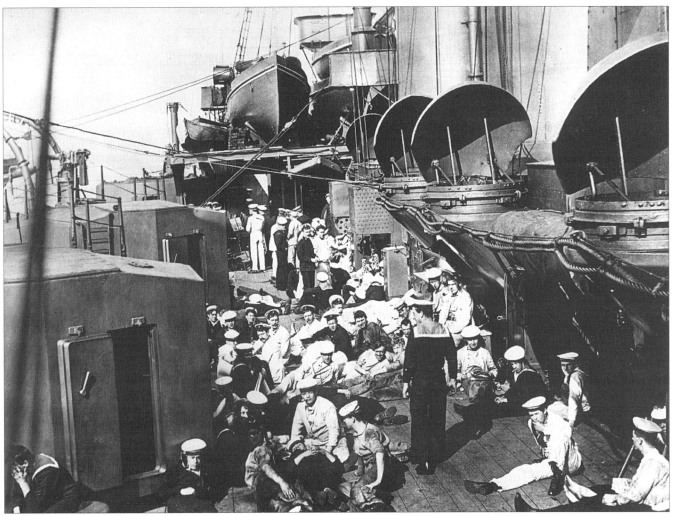

139 Mullett.

Acquisition	Donated by Mrs J Mullet.
Photographer	Mr P J Mullett
Number of Negatives	71
Print Status	Negatives only
Other Material	Photograph album
Access	Numbered

Both merchant and naval vessels from around the turn of the century up to the 1960s are depicted. These images were photographed largely around the south coast of England, Scotland and Germany. Some of the warships, such as HMS *Hood* (1918) and HMS *Nelson* (1925), were photographed during the 1937 Spithead Review.

Facing page:

Top: Seen here, alongside the Thompson fitting-out wharf at Belfast in December 1910, is the White Star liner *Olympic*. Her fourth funnel is yet to be lifted into position. Unlike her sisters, *Titanic* and *Britannic*, the *Olympic* survived to serve with success on the North Atlantic.
Collection: Mullett
NMM Neg. No. P39880

Bottom: This photograph was taken by Lieutenant Fildes RN while serving in the first class armoured cruiser HMS *Natal* in the period 1912–15. Life in the navy was not all work – sailors and marines enjoyed their stand easy.
Collection: Myers
NMM Neg. No. C7137/U

---

140 Myers.

Acquisition	Gift of Mr Bernard Myers
Photographer	Commander Denis Quintin Fildes RN
Number of Negatives	37
Print Status	Printed
Other Material	Photographic prints and a photograph album
Access	Partially catalogued

These images relate to the early career of Denis Fildes, from a midshipman with the cruiser *King Alfred* (1901) in 1906, to a lieutenant on board HMS *Natal* (1905) in 1914. He also served on the destroyer *Waveney* (1903) throughout 1910.
Several scenes show life on board, activities such as physical exercise and a pay parade. In addition to a cutter race, other cruisers anchored at Wei-Hai-Wei, China were also photographed.

Above, this page:
The launch of a ship is a special occasion for the shipyard and Thames Iron Works at Blackwall were justifiably pleased at the successful entry into the water of the battleship *Sans Pareil* on 9 May 1887.
Collection: National Buildings Record
NMM Neg. No. G5571

---

141 National Buildings Record.

Acquisition	Gift of the National Buildings Record
Photographer	Mr H W Taunt
Number of Negatives	15
Print Status	Printed
Access	Numbered, Sorted, Identified

Shipping is depicted on the Thames in the 1880s and 1890s. Some of the negatives depict the battleship *Sans Pareil* on its launching, 9 May 1887, at the Thames Iron Works, Blackwall. Other vessels identified are the cargo vessels *Blonde* (1863) and *Cousins Arbib* (1882), the schooner *Peter Brown* (1855), the four-masted barque *Talavera* (1882) and the cable ship *Dacia* (1867).

142 Nautical Photo Agency.

Acquisition	Gift of Mrs G Poyser
Number of Negatives	30,421
Print Status	Partially printed
Access	Partially catalogued

The Nautical Photo Agency (NPA) collection is the largest single holding of negatives that has been acquired by the Museum and, together with the Richard Perkins collection, forms the backbone of its archive of historic photographs. The NPA was founded by Frank Bowen and Captain F C Poyser to bring together into one collection

the negative holdings of numerous maritime photographers and enthusiasts. It was run by Captain Poyser until his death, upon which the Agency was wound up. Many of the negatives were returned to their owners but the balance was generously presented to the Museum by Mrs Poyser in 1966 and 1975.

This is a comprehensive collection, about two-thirds of which has been catalogued, that covers most aspects of maritime photography. A substantial part consists of views of individual merchant ships through to the 1950s. Most types of sailing ship rig are to be found; large deep-sea craft such as barques, brigs and schooners are well represented, as are the smaller coastal types like ketches, spritsail barges, luggers and smacks.

Steam and motor vessels cover the entire shipping spectrum from harbour tugs and coasters, through general cargo tramps and tankers, to prestigious passenger and cargo liners. British cross-channel ferries and excursion vessels are to be found, along with light vessels, pilot

The Royal Naval College, Greenwich and the Royal Hospital School, from the roof of Inigo Jones' Queen's House. The replica vessel in the foreground is *Fame*, built to assist with the training of the school's pupils. From 1934 the buildings of the Royal Hospital School have been occupied by the National Maritime Museum.
Collection: Melotte NMM Neg. No. G13041

The devastation wrought by the Calcutta cyclone of 5 October 1864 is amply shown in this photograph. Some 200 sea-going vessels were torn from their moorings by the force of the storm and went adrift, of which number only a dozen or so avoided being wrecked on the shore.
Collection: Nautical Photo Agency NMM Neg. No. P134

Under way in Dover Harbour between 1919 and 1922, this is the steam lifeboat *James Stevens No. 3*. Built in 1898, this boat served at Grimsby, Gorleston, Angle Bay, Holyhead and Totland Bay before moving to Dover, her last station.
Collection: Nautical Photo Agency NMM Neg. No. P941

Spectators on Liverpool Landing Stage await the sailing of the Canadian-Pacific liner *Lake Champlain* (1900) at a date between 1903 and 1906. This was a regular scene when Liverpool was one of the premier departure ports for transatlantic passenger services.
Collection: Nautical Photo Agency NMM Neg. No. P15513

The Hudson's Bay Company steamship *Baychimo* (1914) at Vancouver in July 1925. In the summer of 1931 the *Baychimo* left Vancouver on her annual trading voyage northwards but by October had been embayed by ice. Abandoned, the ship disappeared into the Arctic. She was next seen in 1934, drifting with the ice. Reports of sightings continued into the 1960s.
Collection: Nautical Photo Agency NMM Neg. No. P9097

The motor ship *Rangitiki* was built by John Brown & Co. at Clydebank and was completed in 1929. Here, in 1937, members of the crew in bosun's chairs are painting her forefunnel.
Collection: Nautical Photo Agency NMM Neg. No. N47572

service craft and private yachts. A vessel could be found to represent nearly every British shipbuilder and shipowning company of the period. There are numerous negatives of trawlers, drifters and other fishing vessels of deep-sea, coastal and inshore types, both British and foreign, and there are also a few depictions of whalers and sealers. Part of the collection contains topographical material with views of British ports, harbours and lighthouses. Some shots of foreign ports can also be located. Finally, there are about two hundred negatives of British and foreign warships.

143 Navy and Army Illustrated.

Acquisition	Copied from the 'Navy and Army Illustrated'
Number of Negatives	2,312
Print Status	Printed
Access	Numbered, Sorted, Identified

The 'Navy and Army Illustrated' was first published in 1895 as a weekly journal and the first series ceased publication in 1903. These journals were bound into fifteen volumes and fourteen of these have had their maritime pictorial contents copied onto 35mm film (the missing volume covers the period 22 September 1900 to 16 March 1901). The illustrations are all half-tone photographs from various sources and principally depict British warships, both in service and during construction, Royal Navy personnel and life on board ship.

144 Nesdall.

Acquisition	Donated by Mr A J Nesdall
Number of Negatives	14
Print Status	Printed
Access	Fully catalogued

The battleship *Massachusetts* (1941) is shown as a museum ship at Fall River, Massachusetts, USA in 1973.

145 P & O.

Acquisition	Donated by the Peninsular & Oriental Steam Navigation Co
Number of Negatives	2,140
Print Status	Negatives only
Other Material	Photographic prints, photograph albums and transparencies
Access	Sorted

The Peninsular and Oriental Steam Navigation Company began donating photographs and negatives to the Museum in 1973. The majority of the collection comprises colour transparencies, photographic prints and nearly one hundred photograph albums. The earliest negatives feature Orient Steam Navigation Company passenger liners of 1871. Nearly 300 negatives depict the interiors of various Orient Line and Canadian Pacific Line passenger vessels in the 1920s and early 1930s. The bulk of the negatives were taken between 1945 and 1980 and are of ships of the British India Steam Navigation Co, P & O and Strick Line. Various series include educational cruises by the *Dunera* (1937) and *Nevasa* (1956), ore/bulk/oil carriers loading ore at Vitoria, Brazil in 1974 and the hulk of the *Great Britain* (1843) in the Falkland Islands. The remainder of the negatives cover other aspects of the company such as personnel, cargo handling, life at sea, offices and advertising.

There are negatives taken in Ceylon (Sri Lanka), Malaysia and Singapore during various cruises.

146 Padron Albornoz.

Acquisition	Donated by Senor Juan A Padron Albornoz
Number of Negatives	6
Print Status	Printed
Other Material	Photographic prints
Access	Numbered, Sorted, Identified

Probably taken c.1952, the collection includes the harbour at Santa Cruz de Tenerife and the French passenger liner *De Grasse* (1924), the Spanish passenger/cargo liner *Monte Ulia* (1952) and the Panamanian passenger ship *Nelly* (1940), berthed there.

The USA has preserved a large number of its World War II warships including battleships and aircraft carriers. The battleship *Massachusetts*, seen here in 1973, has been in use as a museum/memorial at Fall River since 1965.
**Collection: Nesdall
NMM Neg. No. N29293**

One of the ship's officers at the chart table of the passenger liner *Kenya* (1951). This posed photograph, taken in 1951, is one of a set taken to mark the entry into service of the *Kenya*, which had accommodation for 273 passengers as well as considerable cargo space.
Collection: P & O NMM Neg. No. P39172

The heavy-lift derrick of the Strick Line cargo liner *Shahristan* (1965) is seen here lifting aboard the tug *Rahim*, bound for service in the Persian Gulf. Units of cargo weighing up to 180 tons could be loaded by this means.
Collection: P & O NMM Neg. No. P39170

When the British-India steamer *Mulbera* sailed from the Royal Albert Dock, London for Beira in June 1952, the formalities of customs clearance were carried out in the adjacent transit shed, as close to the ship as possible.
Collection: P & O NMM Neg. No. G4398

147 Paffett.

Acquisition	Gift of Mr J A H Paffett
Number of Negatives	10
Print Status	Printed
Other Material	Lantern slides
Access	Fully catalogued

Taken c.1900–09, these images are of Royal Naval vessels. They include *Inconstant* (1868), *Forth* (1886), *Niger* (1892), *Prince George* (1895), *Renown* (1895), *Aboukir* (1900), *Essex* (1901), and *Patrol* (1904). Some have been identified as being at Devonport and some at Portsmouth.

148 Percival-Prescott.

Acquisition:	Gift of Mr W W Percival-Prescott
Photographer:	Mr W W Percival-Prescott
Number of Negatives:	39
Print Status:	Printed
Other Material:	Photographic prints
Access:	Numbered, Sorted, Identified

Taken by an NMM staff member around Chatham Royal Naval Dockyard, these colour negatives include the Ropery and other dockyard buildings in February 1982.

149 Perkins.

Acquisition	Donated by Mr Richard Perkins
Photographer	Mr Richard Perkins and others
Number of Negatives	12,201
Print Status	Partially printed
Other Material	Albums of warship recognition drawings
Access	Partially catalogued

Richard Perkins was deeply interested in the subject of warship recognition and from 1926 to 1939 he photographed a very large number of warships, auxiliaries and naval harbour craft, principally at Devonport, Dartmouth and Portsmouth. To enable him to study the changes in warship appearance back to 1860 he purchased a number of well-known collections

and also acquired negatives from other photographers and collectors by exchanging some of his own spare negatives. By these means he amassed a comprehensive collection which includes the work of Adamson, Amos, Coates, Cozens, Cribb, Hopkins, Johnson & Logan, Owers, Robertson, Seward, Silk and West.

Immediately after World War II he purchased the wartime negatives of Lieutenant-Commander R D Trimmingham RNVR and Lieutenant-Commander P W Ratcliffe RNVR. He also acquired

Built between 1786 and 1792, the 1,140ft Ropery in Chatham Dockyard is one of the longest brick-built buildings in Europe. Here we see rope yarn being made in February 1982 in the adjacent spinning room.
Collection: Percival-Prescott
NMM Neg. No. C7147/14

HMS *Courageous* was built in 1916 as a large cruiser and completed conversion to an aircraft carrier in May 1928. She was lost in September 1939 to torpedo attack while hunting submarines. She is seen here on 22 July 1934 with HMS *Hood*.
Collection: Perkins
NMM Neg. No. N10446

In May 1937 King George VI reviewed his fleet at Spithead. The First Destroyer Flotilla of the Mediterranean Fleet were present and here we see the *Greyhound* and *Glowworm* dressed overall in Line D.
Collection: Perkins NMM Neg. No. N3091

HMS *Newcastle*, a light cruiser launched by Vickers-Armstrong on the Tyne in 1936, is seen here off Bermuda in 1941. The majority of her service was east of Suez. She was scrapped at Faslane in 1959.
Collection: Perkins NMM Neg. No. N6249

RNVR Captain T D Manning's negatives taken in the wartime period. He stopped taking photographs himself and concentrated his efforts on copying a considerable quantity of large glass-plate negatives onto a smaller format. The surplus large plates are now held at the Imperial War Museum.

The Perkins Collection relates to warships in the period 1860–1946 with the emphasis on British vessels, although a large number of foreign vessels are also included. Most of the photographs were taken in British ports or coastal waters with the exception of the Trimmingham negatives which were taken at Bermuda. The ships depicted range from the ironclad *Warrior* (1860) to the battleship *Rodney* (1925), cruisers of all types from 1860 to 1946, lesser warships, auxiliaries, tugs and tenders, including dockyard launches and lighters.

150   Petherick.

Acquisition	Museum copies from material lent by Captain A Petherick
Number of Negatives	11
Print Status	Printed
Other Material	Photographic prints
Access	Numbered, Sorted, Identified

Taken in 1912, this collection features views of shipping at Bude, including the ketch *Ceres* (1811) and the wreck of the ketch *Elizabeth* (1838).

Ships of the Royal Navy frequently adopt mascots and these come in all shapes and sizes. In September 1921 the battleship *Ajax* had a bear affectionately named 'Trotsky' on board whilst serving in the Black Sea and Dardanelles.
Collection: Pickard
NMM Neg. No. N23193

151   Pickard.

Acquisition	Gift of Mrs P F Pickard
Photographer	Mr. Frederick L S Pickard
Number of Negatives	69
Print Status	Printed
Access	Fully catalogued

The negatives in this group were taken mostly in the eastern Mediterranean in 1921 and 1922. The photographer was a midshipman serving on board HMS *Emperor of India* (1913) and HMS *Ajax* (1912) at the time. HMS *Emperor of India* was photographed dressed overall for the King's birthday in 1921 and Pickard took several views on board when she was being coaled. HMS *Ajax* is shown off Malta, during a variety of training exercises. Her mascot, a bear named 'Trotsky', is shown being returned to her from *Emperor of India*.

Other vessels represented in the collection include the Iron Duke Class battleships *Iron Duke* (1912) and *Benbow* (1913), a number of S Class destroyers, the battleship *King George V* (1911), the battlecruiser *Renown* (1916), the destroyer depot ship *Blenheim* (1890) and the French battleship *Jean Bart* (1911). The paddle dockyard tug *Orient* (1877) is also featured, acting as a liberty boat at Malta. The rest of the collection has scenes of maritime interest taken at various ports in the eastern Mediterranean, including Alexandria, Corfu and Istanbul.

152   Pitts.

Acquisition	Gift of Mr J W C Pitts and Mrs Cooper
Number of Negatives	609
Print Status	Negatives only
Other Material	Photographic prints
Access	Partially catalogued

Both naval and merchant vessels are depicted. The naval vessels were photographed in the 1930s and 1940s. The earliest depiction of merchant vessels dates from 1927 and the latest from the 1960s. Two ceremonial naval reviews at Spithead are also depicted: King George V's Jubilee Review of July 1935 and King George VI's Coronation Review of May 1937. This is when many of the pictures of naval vessels were taken.

Merchant vessels include many well-known passenger liners, cargo liners and ferries of the period.

153 Pollock.

Acquisition	Gift of James Pollock, Sons & Co Ltd
Number of Negatives	60
Print Status	Partially printed
Other Material	Photographic prints and photograph albums
Access	Numbered

The shipyard of James Pollock, Sons and Co Ltd was established at Faversham, Kent, at the beginning of World War I, the firm having previously acted as naval architects and consultants. The company specialised in the building of barges, lighters, tugs, coasters and small tankers. It was also a pioneer in diesel propulsion and in the construction of concrete ships. The yard was closed in 1970. The collection shows assorted craft built by the company between about 1928 and 1935, either on the stocks, being launched or in their completed state. There are also general views of the yard, engines and equipment.

154 Portsmouth Dockyard.

Acquisition	Donated by Portsmouth Dockyard
Number of Negatives	5,269
Print Status	Partially printed
Other Material	Photographic prints.
Access	Numbered, Identified

This is strictly speaking two different collections but they are treated as one because they both came from Portsmouth Dockyard.

The scene in No 13 Dock, Portsmouth Dockyard, on 3 May 1915 during the keel laying of the submarine *J.2*. In the background her sister boat *J.1* is in frame having been laid down seven days earlier. Note that every person is wearing a hat.
Collection: Portsmouth Dockyard NMM Neg. No. G10224

The destroyer *Onslow* berthed below the 240-ton cantilever crane in No. 3 Basin of Portsmouth Dockyard on 25 May 1944. Outboard of her is the frigate *Dacres*, fitted out as Assault Group Headquarters Ship for the invasion of Normandy.
Collection: Portsmouth Dockyard NMM Neg. No. N25494

In 1965 the Ministry of Public Buildings and Works discarded a considerable quantity of glass negatives in Portsmouth Dockyard. 378 were salvaged. These principally relate to the building of major warships at Portsmouth in the period 1905–26, the vessels involved being six battleships, one heavy cruiser and three submarines. The balance of these negatives depict British warships of varying types from ironclads to harbour craft with a date range of 1890 to 1933.

In 1973 Mr R S Horne, the Portsmouth Dockyard historian, passed a large number of negatives to the Museum. These relate to the work undertaken at Portsmouth and by government departments based at the Dockyard during the period 1927–53. There are few individual ship portraits in this acquisition; the emphasis is on the repairing and refitting of vessels. The construction, repair and maintenance of buildings, quays, berths and docks are well covered, many of the buildings being situated in other government establishments in the Portsmouth area including Gosport, Fareham and Calshot. Personnel at work, types of transport, examples of apprentices' work, wooden mock-ups for new vessels and detailed views of ships' underwater fittings are also featured in this collection.

D-Day was less than two weeks away when this photograph was taken on 25 May 1944, looking across from No. 3 Basin, Portsmouth Dockyard, towards Fountain Lake. Moored in trots here are some of the minesweeping and landing ships which would shortly be used in the invasion of Europe.
Collection: Portsmouth Dockyard
NMM Neg. No. N25502

Hospital ships were vital in both World Wars and were usually converted passenger vessels. The *Garth Castle* of 1910 served the Grand Fleet from 1914 to 1919. Her patients are enjoying some fresh air supervised by the medical staff, c.1915.
Collection: Poulton
NMM Neg. No. C4485

155   Poulton.

Acquisition	Museum copies from an album donated by Miss L Poulton
Number of Negatives	32
Print Status	Printed
Other Material	Photograph album
Access	Numbered, Sorted, Identified

The album from which the negatives were copied belonged to W A Batsford, a steward and ward attendant on board the hospital ship *Garth Castle* (1910). A former Union Castle passenger and cargo liner, she was converted into a naval hospital ship in November 1914 and for the duration of World War I was hospital ship to the Grand Fleet, being stationed at Scapa Flow, Cromarty Firth and the Firth of Forth. The depictions date from 1914, 1915, and possibly early 1916. In addition to images of the vessel this collection also includes photographs of the medical staff, operating theatres, wards and cot cases being brought aboard. Some show other naval hospital ships.

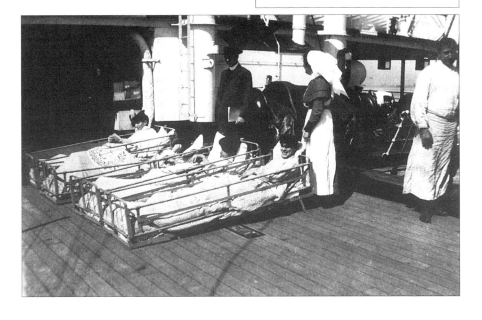

A two-masted Syrian schooner at sea in the Mediterranean between the two World Wars.
Collection: Prins
NMM Neg. No. N41093

156 Prins.

Acquisition	Unknown
Number of Negatives	61
Print Status	Partially printed
Other Material	Photographic prints
Access	Numbered

Eastern Mediterranean sailing craft form the subject of this collection. The majority of the negatives depict Syrian schooners of two main types, two-masted and two-masted topsail. They were taken in the inter-war period.

157 Proctor.

Acquisition	Donated by and copied from photographs lent by Mr D Proctor
Photographer	Mr D Proctor
Number of Negatives	50
Print Status	Partially printed
Other Material	Photographic prints
Access	Partially catalogued

Concerned with the Battle of the Falkland Islands, 1914, this collection shows the battlecruiser *Inflexible* (1907) with battle damage, as well as German prisoners on board. There is also a view of the Bristol Class light cruiser *Glasgow* (1909), in 1914–15, and of the armed merchant cruiser *Otranto* (1909), in December 1914. Other depictions include on-board views of the training ship *Mercury* (1878), taken in 1964; HMS *Unicorn* (1824), in use as a drillship in 1962; and the 1960 replica of the *Bounty* in the Pool of London in 1962.

158 Public Record Office.

Acquisition	Museum copies of photographs transferred from the Public Record Office
Photographer	Mr Jabez Hughes
Number of Negatives	34
Print Status	Printed
Other Material	Photographic prints.
Access	Numbered, Sorted, Identified

Work in progress on the Royal Naval Dockyard extension at Portsmouth between 4 June 1868 and 14 July 1870 is shown in this collection.

Above: The light cruiser HMS *Glasgow* lying stopped in the South Atlantic while operating out of the Falklands Islands in 1914–15.
Collection: Proctor
NMM Neg. No. C6951/B

Left: In the 1860s and 1870s a massive extension to Portsmouth Dockyard was undertaken. This photograph, dated 13 April 1870, shows work proceeding on the construction of No. 12 Dock.
Collection: Public Record Office
NMM Neg. No. C7906/14

The Hain Line cargo steamship *Trelyon* (1898) passes, under tow, on the River Avon as spectators take advantage of what appears to be a fine weekend and a good spot for viewing shipping on the river.
Collection: Randall NMM Neg. No. N46534

Gustaf Erikson's barque *Pommern* (1903) in the English Channel in June 1937, approaching the end of a voyage from Port Germein to London with a cargo of grain.
Collection: Ransome-Wallis NMM Neg. No. N36411

159 Raddings.

Acquisition	Museum copies from negatives lent by Captain J Raddings
Photographer	Mr John Raddings
Number of Negatives	39
Print Status	Partially printed
Other Material	Photographic prints
Access	Numbered, Identified

These images relate to John Raddings' time as a crew member on the three-masted schooner *Jane Banks* (1878) during 1931 and 1932. A number of negatives show the ship at Par, Cornwall, and some show her under sail.

160 Randall.

Acquisition	Donated by Mr G E Frost
Photographer	Mr J Randall
Number of Negatives	302
Print Status	Partially printed
Other Material	Photographic prints
Access	Partially catalogued

Randall photographed merchant shipping on the Avon, at Falmouth and on the Thames from about 1900 to 1938. He was mainly interested in merchant sailing ships but also photographed various types of merchant steamships.

161 Ransome-Wallis.

Acquisition	Bequest of Dr P Ransome-Wallis
Photographer	Dr P Ransome-Wallis
Number of Negatives	7,335
Print Status	Partially printed
Other Material	Photographic prints, photograph albums and transparencies
Access	Fully catalogued

Dr P Ransome-Wallis was a well-known photographer and writer on railways and shipping. His impressive collection of railway negatives was bequeathed to the National Railway Museum, York, and the NMM acquired his shipping material in 1985. Dr Ransome-Wallis started taking photographs of ships at Immingham in 1924. He travelled widely and in the next sixty years visited most European countries, the USA, Canada, the West Indies, South Africa, Australia, Hong Kong and the Mediterranean. In September 1939 he joined the Royal Navy and in September 1940 he was posted to the light cruiser *Dido* (1939) in which he served until December 1941. For the rest of the war period he was stationed at HMS *Osprey*, the anti-submarine training school at Dunoon, and carried out one return voyage across the Atlantic on convoy duty in the spring of 1944.

His primary interests in maritime affairs were passenger carrying ships and ferries, especially ships owned by railway companies. He was a regular visitor to the south coast ports of Dover, Folkestone, Newhaven and Southampton and also attended the five naval reviews held at Spithead between 1935 and 1977.

162   Rayner.

Acquisition	Bequest of H C Rayner MBE
Number of Negatives	30
Print Status	Printed
Other Material	Photographic prints, photograph albums and postcards
Access	Fully catalogued

Rayner was an avid collector of postcards, mainly of warships, and his collection of over 30,000 cards forms an important part of the Museum's reference archive. He also bequeathed a small number of negatives, which depict warships in 1918 in British waters. Half of the negatives are of British and American battleships of the Grand Fleet; the remainder are of lesser war vessels.

The broadside ironclad HMS *Achilles* at sea with the Channel Fleet in 1884, with the masted turret ship *Neptune* just discernible over her forecastle.
Collection: Richards
NMM Neg. No. N11300

Photographed in mid-Atlantic whilst in convoy during 1944, this is the Canadian-Pacific cargo liner *Beaverhill* (1928). Accommodation for 138 passengers was added in 1941 and this accounts for the large number of life-rafts carried. The *Beaverhill* went aground at St John, New Brunswick, in November 1944 and became a loss.
Collection: Ransome-Wallis NMM Neg. No. N33097

The former German submarine *U1105* (unofficially named *Black Panther*) in the floating dock *AFD 7* in Holy Loch in October 1945. This boat commissioned for trials in the Royal Navy in June 1945 before going to the USA in 1946.
Collection: Ransome-Wallis NMM Neg. No. N32108

163 Richards.

Acquisition	Gift of S T A Richards
Number of Negatives	19
Print Status	Printed
Access	Fully catalogued

The ironclad battleships *Achilles* (1863), *Agincourt* (1865), *Minotaur* (1863) and *Northumberland* (1866), all of the Channel Squadron, are shown in 1884.

164 Rivington.

Acquisition	Purchased from, and copied from an album lent by, Mr H J F Thompson
Photographer	Reverend J Rivington, naval chaplain
Number of Negatives	32
Print Status	Printed
Access	Partially catalogued

The earliest of the negatives were taken by the Reverend J Rivington when he was serving as chaplain on board HMS *Temeraire* (1876), in 1880–81. There is also a portrait of Sir Charles Cust RN taken in 1884. The later negatives were taken at Portsmouth between c.1896 and 1903. There is a depiction of a khaki field piece, used by the Naval Brigade in the siege of Ladysmith, on board HMS *Powerful* (1895) in April 1900. There is also the War Department tender *Collingwood Dickson* (1889) moored on HM Gunwharf at the Camber, Portsmouth.

165 Robinson.

Acquisition	Gift of Captain J R Robinson
Number of Negatives	55
Print Status	Negatives only
Access	Numbered, Identified

Newhaven, on the Sussex coast, underwent substantial improvements in the 1880s and a number of negatives in this collection show the breakwater under construction. Other negatives depict storm damage to the sea wall in 1890 and general views of the harbour, 1870–1900. The collection also contains some Edwardian views of Bournemouth, the paddle steamer *Monarch* (1888), Loch Eck and Loch Long.

The Alaska Packers Association iron ship *Star of France*, built in 1877 by Harland & Wolff, Belfast. The ship's first owner was J P Corry & Co of Belfast, who employed her in the Calcutta trade.
Collection: San Francisco Maritime Museum
NMM Neg. No. P8182

HMS *Temeraire* of 1876 was a central battery/barbette ship and was the largest brig-rigged vessel ever built. Some of her crew are shown at small arms drill on 19 April 1881, when the ship visited Cagliari, Sardinia.
Collection: Rivington
NMM Neg. No. C3752

166 Royal Institution of Naval Architects.

Acquisition	Museum copies from an album donated by the Royal Institution of Naval Architects
Photographer	Mr G Washington Wilson and Mr J Valentine
Number of Negatives	30
Print Status	Printed
Other Material	Photograph albums
Access	Numbered, Sorted, Identified

Late nineteenth-century Scottish scenes are depicted, with a strong emphasis on fishing. Places represented include Aberdeen, Peterhead, Wick, Stornoway, Lerwick, Pittenweem, Anstruther, St Monance, the Isle of Arran and the Tay and Forth Bridges.

167 San Francisco Maritime Museum.

Acquisition	Donated by the San Francisco Maritime Museum
Photographer	Mr William Muir
Number of Negatives	38
Print Status	Partially printed
Other Material	Photographic prints
Access	Fully catalogued

This collection features ships, barques and schooners in the first three decades of the twentieth century. A high proportion show vessels of the Alaska Packers Association.

168 Scott Lithgow.

Acquisition	Museum copies from albums lent by Scott Lithgow Ltd
Number of Negatives	74
Print Status	Printed
Other Material	Photographic prints
Access	Numbered, Sorted, Identified

Scotts' Shipbuilding and Engineering Company Ltd yard, and vessels under construction between about 1914 and 1937 form

the subject of this collection. This Greenock-based company, dating from 1711, is the oldest shipbuilding company in the world and undertook both merchant and naval work. Although still extant it has now ceased shipbuilding.
The most complete coverage is given to the building of the submarine *Swordfish (S1)* of 1916 but the cruiser *Dragon* (1917) and destroyers *Westminster* (1918) and *Windsor* (1918) are also quite well represented. Some merchant ships are also included.

During World War I the threat of submarine attack on British ports was sufficient to persuade the government to stretch defensive booms across principal estuaries. Here the steam barge *Rosie* (1907) is working on the Humber Boom.
Collection: Sharples
NMM Neg. No. N18542

HMS *Dragon* fitting out at Scott's Greenock shipyard on 18 March 1918. Before completion her bridge was remodelled to incorporate an aircraft hangar. The war-standard tanker *War Angler* is completing in the basin alongside.
Collection: Scott Lithgow
NMM Neg. No. D1478

HMS *Odin* was one of a class of six sloops built by Sheerness Dockyard in 1901–04 and these were the last sloops to be built with a sailing capability. The photograph was taken in October 1902 on completion of fitting out.
Collection: Sheerness Dockyard NMM Neg. No. N11443

A view over Grand Harbour and the town of Valletta, on the island of Malta, in the early 1960s. The Shell tanker *Achatina* (1958) is entering the harbour, passing Fort St Angelo. In the foreground is the transport ferry *Empire Petrel* (1945).
Collection: Shell Oil NMM Neg. No. P36203

169 Scudder.

Acquisition	Donated by Mr and Mrs W L Scudder
Number of Negatives	10
Print Status	Negatives only
Other Material	Photographic prints
Access	Fully catalogued

A variety of vessels are shown: they include the *Great Eastern* (1858), taken while she was laid up at Milford Haven in 1881, and the *Foudroyant* (1798), which was a former wooden Second Rate used as a training ship. She is shown ashore on Blackpool beach between June and November 1897.
Also included are negatives of the *Britannia* (1860) at Dartmouth, *Berengaria* (1912) and *Majestic* (1921) at Southampton, *Prometheus* (1896), *Golden Eagle* (1909) and *Lorna Doone* (1891).

170 Sharples.

Acquisition	Donated by Miss Sharples
Number of Negatives	10
Print Status	Printed
Access	Fully catalogued

This series of negatives shows vessels working on the Humber Boom during World War I. There are two tugs, the *Robie* (1915) and the *Terrier* (1883), two gate vessels *Glengoil* (1882) and *Hubbuck* (1886) and also the steam barge *Rosie* (1907). The water tender *Borderglen* (1913) is shown at Grimsby.

171 Sheerness Dockyard.

Acquisition	Museum copies from material lent via Captain PMB Chavasse.
Number of Negatives	207.
Print Status	Printed
Other Material	Photographic prints.
Access	Fully catalogued

In Febuary 1958 it was announced that Sheerness Dockyard was to close. As a result the Museum received a number of items relating to the work of the yard, including a large number of photographs of British warships. These photographs have been copied and they are of vessels built between 1870 and 1916 which were commissioned or refitted at Sheerness. With just two exceptions, all of the ships depicted were photographed prior to 1905 and the majority of the vessels are sloops, torpedo gunboats, gunvessels and small cruisers.

172 Shell Oil.

Acquisition	Gift of Shell Oil UK
Number of Negatives	37
Print Status	Printed
Other Material	A photographic print and transparencies
Access	Fully catalogued

There are twenty Shell Oil tankers of British and Dutch flag depicted in this collection, ranging in launch date from 1954 to 1975. The vessels are *Acavus* (1958), *Achatina* (1958), *Daphnella* (1966), *Donacilla* (1966), *Dorcasia* (1967), *Heldia* (1955), *Hemimactra* (1956), *Hindsia* (1955), *Hinnites* (1956), *Kelletia* (1957), *Kopionella* (1955), *Korenia* (1955), *Lembulus* (1974), *Limnea* (1975), *Macoma* (1968), *Opalia* (1963), *Sepia* (1961), *Shell Charaima* (1954), *Solen* (1961) and *Volvula* (1956).

173 Shepheard-Walwyn.

Acquisition	Copied from photographs lent by Mrs Shepheard-Walwyn
Number of Negatives	15
Print Status	Printed
Other Material	Photographic prints
Access	Numbered, Identified

Taken about 1865, these photographs show the battleships *Lord Clyde* (1864), *Black Prince* (1861), and *Ocean* (1863), the wooden despatch vessel *Psyche* (1862), and the sloop *Queen* (1839). There are also depictions of groups of officers who appear to have served on board the *Black Prince* in the 1862–64 period.

174 Shipping World and Shipbuilder.

Acquisition	Gift of Mr Derek H Deere, Editor
Number of Negatives	39
Print Status	Printed
Other Material	Photographic prints
Access	Fully catalogued

Two passenger liners are shown being fitted out at Monfalcone, Italy in 1965 and three cargo vessels completing in Finland, Germany and the Netherlands in 1967.

The Home Lines' turbine passenger liner *Oceanic* is seen here at Algeciras in April 1965 on her maiden voyage from Genoa to New York. The *Oceanic* was intended for her owner's Cuxhaven to New York service but was employed primarily in cruising from New York.
Collection: Shipping World and Shipbuilder NMM Neg. No. N24325

Looking across Barry Docks, in South Wales, in 1911. These docks, the first of which was opened in 1889, were built for the export of coal from the Welsh coalfield. In 1910 3,267 vessels loaded at Barry.
Collection: Shirvington NMM Neg. No. G3855

Part of the timber deck cargo of the British tramp steamship *Induna* (1925) going over the side after shifting during a voyage from Port Alberni, Canada, to Kobe, in Japan.
Collection: Simpson NMM Neg. No. N45925

175 Shirvington.

Acquisition	Gift of Mr Mallett and Mr Owen
Photographer	Mr Heber Shirvington and Catford Brothers
Number of Negatives	33
Print Status	Printed
Access	Numbered, Sorted, Identified

Of the negatives in this collection taken by Shirvington, most depict vessels around South Glamorgan, Wales, particularly at Barry. There are portraits of unidentified seamen, one of whom is on board HMS *Suffolk* (1926).

Three of the vessels are shown wrecked or damaged, including *Zingara* (1898) in 1919, *Walkure* (1907) and *Verajean* (1891), both in 1908. *Oxfordshire* (1912) is shown as a hospital ship. The paddle steamer *Gwalia* (1905), run by the Barry Railway Company, is depicted off Barry Pier with passengers aboard. General port activity also includes views of Barry pilot boats.

The negatives taken by Catford Brothers show a salvage operation undertaken on *Ackworth* (1889). The vessel is being refloated from Lundy Island, Devon, in 1892.

176 Simpson.

Acquisition	Donated by Mrs M Simpson
Number of Negatives	92
Print Status	Negatives only
Other Material	Photographic prints and postcards
Access	Numbered, Identified

These images relate to the career of Captain Stanley L R Simpson, who died in 1975. Many of the negatives date from his time on board the tramp *Induna* (1925) in the early 1930s. This vessel was owned by Maclay and McIntyre Ltd and employed in long distance tramp trades.

The *Induna* is shown loading timber at Port Alberni, British Columbia, Canada, suffering a broken mainmast and shifting cargo, on a voyage to Kobe, Japan, and coaling at St Lucia, West Indies.

The fishing port of Lowestoft, in Suffolk, developed rapidly in the second half of the nineteenth century and by 1898, about which time this photograph was taken, had 480 sailing drifters and trawlers registered there. Most of the vessels shown carry the local 'LT' registration but the boat nearest the camera is a visitor; the *Criterion* of Ramsgate.
Collection: Smiths, Suitall NMM Neg. No. P27504

177 Smiths, Suitall.

Acquisition	Donated by Messrs Smiths, Suitall Ltd
Number of Negatives	35
Print Status	Printed
Other Material	Photographic prints and postcards
Access	Numbered, Sorted, Identified

This collection features views of Ipswich (the river and docks), Rowhedge and East Runton, the harbour at Lowestoft, Felixstowe and the Felixstowe to Bawdsey ferry, Shotley and the training ships of HMS *Ganges*. The images probably date from the 1890s to the outbreak of World War I and are some of the best that the Museum has of the places listed.

178 Sotheby's.

Acquisition	Copied from photographs in an album purchased at Sotheby's
Number of Negatives	50
Print Status	Printed
Other Material	Photographic prints and a photograph album
Access	Numbered, Sorted, Identified

The majority of the negatives in this collection cover the building of the Royal Sovereign Class battleship *Royal Oak* (1892) by Laird Bros, Birkenhead. The remaining negatives show the Birkenhead Ironworks, Laird's fitting-out basin, HMS *Talbot* (1895), Portsmouth Harbour and HMS *Victory* (1765).

179 South Eastern Gas Board.

Acquisition	Donated by the South Eastern Gas Board
Photographer	Mr A G Gostelow
Number of Negatives	11
Print Status	Negatives only
Other Material	Photographic prints and photograph albums
Access	Fully catalogued

The South Eastern Gas Board's motor launch *Beverley* (1937) is shown on the Thames, up-stream from Putney Bridge. Also included in the collection are the collier *Dulwich* (1957) in a heavy sea and a view of the Richmond footbridge.

180 Spinney.

Acquisition:	Copied from photographs and an album lent by Mr J D Spinney
Number of Negatives:	24
Print Status:	Printed
Other Material:	Photographic prints
Access:	Numbered, Sorted, Identified

Many of these negatives show Peninsular and Oriental Steam Navigation Co liners (mostly of the 1870s) alongside in the Outer Dock, Southampton, before P and O moved its passenger terminus to London in 1881. There are also negatives dating from the 1880s and 1890s which show scenes at some of the ports visited by the P and O liners. Also shown are the submarine *W1* (1914) on the Tyne in 1915 and the forward and midship guns of HMS *Queen Mary* (1912) in 1913.

181 Stanley.

Acquisition	Gift of the Society for Nautical Research
Photographer	Miss Anne Stanley
Number of Negatives	251
Print Status	Partially printed
Other Material	Photographic prints
Access	Fully catalogued

Gustaf Erikson, the well-known owner of the last fleet of merchant sailing ships, died in August 1947. The following year two of his ships went out to Australia to bring back the last ever Australian grain cargoes to be carried in large square-rigged sailing vessels. The *Passat* (1911), a four-masted barque, sailed from Port Talbot, Wales, on 18 December 1948 with Miss Anne Stanley aboard to record the outward voyage to Port Victoria with her camera. Miss Stanley photographed many aspects of life on board. The crew are shown at work and play, on deck and in the rigging. The *Passat* anchored off Port Victoria on 30 March 1949 and berthed there on 6 April.

Above: Unbending an upper topsail prior to changing the sail aboard the four-masted barque *Passat* (1911). The photograph was taken on 26 January 1949, on passage from Port Talbot to Port Victoria, Australia.
Collection: Stanley NMM Neg. No. P8372

Facing page:
Top: The scene at the Birkenhead shipyard of Laird Brothers on 29 May 1890 for the keel laying of the battleship *Royal Oak*, one of eight provided under the Naval Defence Act of 1889.
Collection: Sothebys NMM Neg. No. C6182

Left: Crossing the Line aboard Erikson's barque *Passat* on 13 January 1949. The 'barber' is at work with his enormous razor on an unfortunate first-timer.
Collection: Stanley NMM Neg. No. P8339

Right: Looking forward, and down on to the deck, from the mizzen royal of the Finnish four-masted barque *Passat* under sail in light airs on 20 January 1949.
Collection: Stanley NMM Neg. No. P8361

182 Stevenson.

Acquisition	Donated by Mr D Alan Stevenson
Number of Negatives	9
Print Status	Negatives only
Access	Numbered, Sorted, Identified

Half of these negatives were taken at the Spithead Review of 24 June 1911 and the photographer has concentrated on the merchant ships present, with views of the Royal Mail Steam Packet Co's *Thames* (1890) and T Wilson & Sons Co Ltd's *Eskimo* (1910). The second class protected cruiser *Dido* (1896) taken in 1906–7, is also worthy of mention.

183 Stuart Bruce.

Acquisition	Bequest of Mr Stuart Bruce
Number of Negatives	150
Print Status	Printed
Other Material	Photographic prints and a postcard
Access	Numbered, Identified

The majority of images in the Stuart Bruce collection were taken in the Shetland Isles over a period from 1900 to 1939. The emphasis is on local craft including fifies, zulus and fourerns. A number of vessels from the North of Scotland, Orkney and Shetland Shipping Co Ltd are also depicted. The balance of the collection comprises views taken on the River Forth, the River Thames and the south Cornish coast.

The coronation of King George V in 1911 was marked by a review of the Fleet at Spithead in June of that year. In this photograph the Wilson liner *Eskimo* (1910) is at anchor as part of the representation of the merchant navy. Beyond, warships of both British and foreign navies fire their salute.
Collection: Stevenson NMM Neg. No. P28617

Loading dried fish into an old sixern on Whalsay, in the Shetland Isles, in 1899. Sixerns derived their name from their provision for three pairs of oars.
Collection: Stuart Bruce NMM Neg. No. P32619

184 Studland Belle.

Acquisition	Museum copies from material lent by Mrs Masters
Number of Negatives	11
Print Status	Printed
Access	Fully catalogued

Studland Bay, Dorset is the location depicted in the majority of these negatives. The paddle steamers *Audrey* (1897) and *Studland Belle* (1904) are also shown. The photographs were taken in the period 1910–14.

185 Sullivan.

Acquisition	Gift of Mr W Sullivan
Number of Negatives	63
Print Status	Negatives only
Other Material	Photographic prints
Access	Fully catalogued

These negatives were all taken in Malta between 1946 and 1950, except for two shot at Marseilles. The majority depict various types of merchant ships in Grand Harbour. These include passenger liners, troopships, general cargo vessels and short-sea traders. Five negatives show warships in Grand Harbour and five are of general views of it. The general quality of the negatives is poor.

186 Sunderland Public Libraries.

Acquisition: Copied from photographs lent by Sunderland Public Libraries

Number of Negatives: 81
Print Status: Partially printed
Access: Partially catalogued

The majority of the collection relates to the Sunderland shipbuilders Robert Thompson and Sons (established in 1854 and wound up in 1933). A few negatives show vessels on the stocks and being launched, but most show some of the firm's output on completion, either alongside at Sunderland or on trials. There are some views of ships under repair by Thompson's.

187 Superb.

Acquisition Transferred from the Ministry of Defence, Bath

Number of Negatives 18
Print Status Printed
Other Material Photographic prints
Access Fully catalogued

The light cruiser HMS *Superb* (1943) was moored off the Swan Hunter shipyard at Wallsend-on-Tyne in November 1945 during her trials period. These negatives were taken on board at this time and give a good impression of the deck layout of the ship.

188 Talbot.

Acquisition Donated by Miss M T Talbot
Photographer Reverend Richard Calvert Jones, Mr Nicolaas Henneman and William Henry Fox Talbot
Number of Negatives 34
Print Status Printed
Other Material Photographic prints
Access Numbered, Sorted, Identified

In September 1934 Miss Matilda Theresa Talbot, of Lacock Abbey, made a gift of 34 calotype negatives

Damage to the France, Fenwick collier *Lockwood* (1896) sustained in collision with the cross-channel steamer *Le Nord* (1898) on 1 March 1912. The *Le Nord* rammed and sank a German submarine during World War I.
Collection: Sunderland Public Libraries
NMM Neg. No. G12095

and 24 original prints to the Museum via Admiral G A Ballard. Miss Talbot was the granddaughter of William Henry Fox Talbot and inherited the estate on the death of her uncle, Charles Henry Talbot, in 1916. She was appointed MBE in 1919, CBE in 1947 and donated Lacock Abbey to The National Trust in 1944. She died in March 1958 at the age of 86.

W H Fox Talbot (1800–77) is rightly regarded as the father of photography as we know it. He was an amateur scientist who gave us the negative-positive system of photography and the first successful form of negative was the calotype. The 34 calotype negatives which Miss Talbot presented are difficult to attribute to individual photographers. It is reasonable to

assume that the majority of the Swansea negatives were taken by the Reverend Calvert Jones and the negatives taken at Plymouth and on board HMS *Superb* (1842) are probably the work of Nicolaas Henneman. Other locations are Malta, Dublin, Naples and Rouen. There are two views of the Royal Hospital, Greenwich, one view of the *Great Britain* (1843) at Bristol and two shipboard scenes. All of the negatives are dated 1845 or earlier.

The light cruiser HMS *Superb* was built by Swan Hunter at Wallsend-on-Tyne from 1942 to 1945 and is shown moored off the shipyard in November 1945. This view taken from the mainmast shows the hospital ship *Toscana* (1923), formerly an Italian vessel.
Collection: Superb NMM Neg. No. N18235

189 Tanner.

Acquisition:	Gift of the Reverend E V Tanner
Photographer:	Reverend E V Tanner
Number of Negatives:	134
Print Status:	Negatives only
Access:	Numbered

The Reverend Tanner took his photographs along the central south coast of England from Portsmouth to Weymouth. His interests centred on warships and large passenger liners and his photographs were taken either in 1913–14 or in the 1930s, with a few notable exceptions. Twenty-six of the negatives depict Royal Navy battleships; 9 are of aircraft carriers; 22 are of fleet assemblies, mainly at Portland, and 43 are of ocean-going passenger liners at Southampton.

190 Tebbutt.

Acquisition	Donated by Mrs O M Tebbutt
Number of Negatives	10
Print Status	Printed
Other Material	Photographic prints
Access	Fully catalogued

This small collection depicts Boston prawners taken in about 1936, and includes scenes on deck during fishing operations.

191 Tenby Museum.

Acquisition	Museum copies from an album lent by Mr J Tipton, Tenby Museum
Number of Negatives	26
Print Status	Printed
Other Material	Photographic prints
Access	Numbered, Sorted, Identified

This collection shows some British warships extant in the 1860 to 1880s period. The vessels, built between 1796 and 1871, include the following: *Canopus* (1796), *Excellent* (1810), *St Vincent* (1815), *Fisgard* (1819), *Britannia* (1820), *Royal Adelaide* (1828), *Rodney* (1833), *Trafalgar* (1841), *Sans Pareil* (1851), *Valorous* (1851), *Princess Royal*

Nicolaas Henneman, one of the earliest exponents of photography, may well have been responsible for this photograph of Greenwich Pensioners, taken c.1845. They are shown by Rysbrack's statue of George II in the Hospital's Grand Square. In the background is Inigo Jones' Queen's House, now part of the Museum.
Collection: Talbot
NMM Neg. No. C3607

Looking aft along the starboard side of the White Star liner *Majestic* (1921) at the Ocean Terminal, Southampton, in April 1931. It is just possible to see the stagings from which members of the crew are painting the funnels.
Collection: Tanner
NMM Neg. No. N63678

(1853), *Marlborough* (1855), *Liffey* (1856), *Topaze* (1858), *Narcissus* (1859), *Gibraltar* (1860), *Howe* (1860), *Newcastle* (1860), *Aurora* (1861), *Rattlesnake* (1861), *Undaunted* (1861), *Wolverine* (1863), *Endymion* (1865) and *Arrow* (1871).

192 Texaco Overseas Tankship Ltd.

Acquisition	Presented by Texaco Overseas Tankship Ltd
Number of Negatives	26
Print Status	Negatives only
Other Material	Photographic prints and transparencies
Access	Fully catalogued

The vessels depicted are oil tankers of Texaco Overseas Tankship Ltd. Most of the negatives show *Caltex Dublin* (1945) during and after berthing at Ras Tanura in Saudi Arabia in March 1959. The on-board views feature Captain Paddon and Mrs Paddon, the Second Officer, the Ras Tanura harbour pilot, the Director of Customs for Ras Tanura and the Shipping Agency representative. There are also views of the 1953 tankers *Caltex Canberra* and *Caltex Manchester*, the former under way at Stockholm and the latter at anchor in an unidentified port.

Below: In 1908 the broadside ironclad HMS *Agincourt* (1865) was converted to a coaling hulk for use at Sheerness. Some of her original fittings were retained and this tiled stove was still in place in a cabin beneath the poop on 21 September 1960.
Collection: Thompson
NMM Neg. No. N16884

193 Thompson.

Acquisition	Donated by Rear-Admiral Thompson
Number of Negatives	9
Print Status	Printed
Access	Fully catalogued

This is a series of negatives taken on board the coaling hulk *C109* (1865), the former armoured broadside ship *Agincourt*, in September 1960, just before it was scrapped. There are detailed views of the interior, including the former seamen's wash-house and a tiled stove in a cabin.

Facing page:
Top: An evocative picture taken in the foundry of John I Thornycroft's Woolston shipyard in about 1912. A tie, cloth cap and waistcoat appear to be the standard form of attire. Protective clothing is notable by its absence.
Collection: Thornycroft
NMM Neg. No. G12865

Bottom: The twin-screw air-sea rescue launch *2661* was built by J Meakes of Marlow using parts prefabricated at Hampton by John I Thornycroft and Co. She is shown undergoing speed trials in the Thames on 23 May 1944.
Collection: Thornycroft
NMM Neg. No. N13315

Below right: The flat-iron gunboat HMS *Arrow* of 1871, moored in the Thames off Greenwich while attached to the Royal Naval College. The old Fifth Rate HMS *Fisgard* of 1819 was used as an accommodation ship here from 1873 to 1878.
Collection: Tenby Museum
NMM Neg. No. D2156

194 Thornycroft.

Acquisition	Gift of Vosper Thornycroft (UK) Ltd
Number of Negatives	7,979
Print Status	Partially printed
Other Material	Photographic prints and photograph albums
Access	Fully catalogued

John I Thornycroft was born in 1843 and his first venture at boat-building was a steam launch named *Nautilus* which he completed in 1862. In 1866 the Chiswick shipyard on the River Thames commenced operations and in 1904 the Woolston shipyard of Mordey, Carney & Co was purchased. Sites were also acquired at Basingstoke (vehicles, engines and armaments), Hampton-on-Thames (wooden vessels), Reading (engines) and Northam (ship repair and lay-up). The success of the company resulted in many orders for wooden-built boats being sub-contracted to other builders, with Thornycrofts providing the drawings, specifications and, in many cases, the machinery. World War I saw the company stretched to the limit to meet its commitments and in 1939 war work again provided full order books for all branches of the company. The Singapore yard, which had been acquired in 1924, was taken over by

the Japanese in 1942 but reverted in 1945. Bombing disrupted production at Woolston but the yard remained open and in the period 1939–45 eighteen destroyers, five escort sloops and one fast minelayer were built. The company also built large numbers of motor craft including air-sea rescue vessels, motor torpedo boats, torpedo recovery and target towing launches and many other fast motor boats. Thornycroft also acted as a parent firm for various landing craft, providing plans, machinery and supervisory staff. Repairs were carried out to a total of 4,486 vessels, excluding small boats and launches, in the same period. During peacetime the company has produced a very wide range of vessels. Warships have included destroyers, sloops, minesweepers, gunboats, motor torpedo boats and coastal motor boats; many of these have been to the order of foreign governments. Merchant shipping types constructed have included small passenger liners, tankers, general cargo ships, shallow draught river steamers, ferries and cattle carriers. In the leisure field there have been motor yachts, cabin

cruisers, racing hydroplanes and houseboats. Among the more unusual craft have been a water purifying punt for use on the Serpentine and a weed dredger for the Royal Military Canal in Kent. The negative collection covers almost every aspect of the work of the company from its inception up to the mid-1950s. Vessels are shown under construction, fitting out, on trials and under repair. The various company yards are well depicted with particular emphasis on Woolston and Hampton.

A busy scene in Thornycroft's Northam shipyard on 28 June 1944. The majority of vessels are tank and infantry landing craft in for repair following the D-Day landings.
**Collection: Thornycroft
NMM Neg. No. N12969**

195 Thyne.

Acquisition	Donated by Dr George Thyne
Photographer	Dr George Thyne
Number of Negatives	94
Print Status	Printed
Access	Fully catalogued

Dr Thyne served as midshipman on board HMS *Lion* (1910). The negatives were taken between May 1917 and June 1919. The majority are of HMS *Lion* with a few other warships of World War I, as well as the surrendered German Fleet at Scapa Flow.

196 Tomlinson.

Acquisition	Gift of Miss Barbara Tomlinson
Photographer	Mr Tomlinson
Number of Negatives	6
Print Status	Printed
Other Material	Photographic prints
Access	Numbered, Sorted, Identified

Boxes of apples are shown packed into the hold of the Blue Star line cargo vessel *Colorado Star* (1952) in February 1961.

197 Turner.

Acquisition	Gift of Miss P J Turner
Photographer	Engineer Lieutenant W G Turner RNR
Number of Negatives	515
Print Status	Negatives only
Other Material	Photographic prints, photograph albums and postcards
Access	Numbered

The majority of the images relate to W G Turner's service on the armed merchant cruisers *Orama* (1911) and *Orbita* (1915). It is probable that he served aboard the *Orama* from 1914 until its loss in 1917 and then aboard the *Orbita* until the end of the war. In addition to a large number of depictions of the *Orama* and the *Orbita* there are many other naval and merchant vessels featured during this wartime period. Places depicted include ports in the south of England, the Mediterranean, South Africa and South America. The balance of the collection is a random mix of merchant ship photographs ranging in date from 1893 to 1964.

198 Tvedt.

Acquisition	Donated by Mrs J A Tvedt
Photographer	Mr J A Tvedt
Number of Negatives	Approximately 700
Print Status	Negatives only; unsorted and currently unavailable
Other Material	Photographic prints and transparencies

Concerned with the British fishing industry in the 1970s and 1980s, this collection mostly depicts fishing vessels at sea, in port, under repair and being built. Mr Tvedt was a naval architect with either the Ministry of Agriculture and Fisheries or the White Fish Authority. He was also with British United Trawlers Ltd of Hull.

199 Underhill.

Acquisition	Bequest of Mr Harold A Underhill
Photographer	Mr H A Underhill
Number of Negatives	127
Print Status	Negatives only
Other Material	Photographic prints and photograph albums
Access	Partially catalogued

Harold Underhill was a very well-known authority on merchant sailing ships and the negatives in this collection reflect this interest. His book 'Masting and Rigging', first published in 1946, has been reprinted many times and still has not been bettered.

The Orient Line passenger liner *Orama*, built on Clydebank in 1911, was converted to an armed merchant cruiser in 1914 and is seen here at Simonstown in that role in 1917. In October of that year, whilst on convoy escort duty, she was torpedoed and sunk by the German submarine *U-62*.
Collection: Turner
NMM Neg. No. N46039

200 Union-Castle.

Acquisition	Gift of the Bricom Group Ltd, Dorking
Number of Negatives	Approximately 5,000
Print Status	Negatives only
Other Material	Photographic prints, photograph albums and transparencies
Access	Sorted

In 1956 the British and Commonwealth Shipping Company Ltd was formed to unite the Union-Castle Mail Steamship Company Ltd, Clan Line and Bullard King groups under one umbrella organisation. This substantial collection reflects the vessels and activities of that company.
It includes vessels from the Union-Castle Mail Steamship Company Ltd and from the Union Line and the Castle Mail Packet Company Ltd, before and after their merger in 1900. The Union Line and the Castle Mail Packet Company Ltd were mainly involved in the transportation of passengers, cargo and mail, particularly to South Africa.
Some of the material is post-World War II. It includes views of the company's ships in port and under way, from sea level and from the air. There are a large number of

negatives taken on board ships showing passenger and crew activities.

There is also material relating to the administration of the companies, with negatives of office buildings, staff at work, leisure activities, personnel and so on.

201 Upham.

Acquisition	Gift of Captain N Upham
Photographer	Captain N Upham
Number of Negatives	53
Print Status	Partially printed
Access	Numbered

These negatives were taken in October 1980 and show views in and around Port Said, Egypt, including the Suez Canal Engineering Works at Port Fuad.

Top: The Union-Castle liner *Edinburgh Castle* (1948) is seen here from the deck of the new Union-Castle liner *Transvaal Castle* on the latter's maiden voyage early in 1962.
Collection: Union-Castle
NMM Neg. No. P39167

Middle: Miss Shirley Oppenheim, one of the Purserettes on board the Union-Castle liner *Transvaal Castle* (1961), attends to a passenger at the purser's bureau during the ship's maiden voyage from Southampton to Cape Town and Durban in January 1962.
Collection: Union-Castle
NMM Neg. No. P39168

Bottom: A small part of the kitchen and servery space of the Union-Castle Line's liner *Transvaal Castle* (1961). This photograph was also taken during the ship's maiden voyage in January 1962.
Collection: Union-Castle
NMM Neg. No. P39169

202   Vaughan.

Acquisition	Donated by Captain H R H Vaughan OBE RN
Photographer	Paymaster Lieutenant-Commander Vaughan
Number of Negatives	481
Print Status	Printed
Other Material	Photographic prints
Access	Numbered

This is a collection of sailing craft photographed by Paymaster Lieutenant-Commander Vaughan RN in the period 1928–30 when he was serving in HMS *Triad* (1909) on the Persian Gulf Station as secretary to the Senior Naval Officer, Captain H Boyes CMG RN.

Most types of local craft of the Persian Gulf and Red Sea are depicted. They are shown under construction, being repaired, laid up and at work. There are also some views of local craft of the Aegean and at Kyrenia taken in the same period.

203   Vickers.

Acquisition	Donated by Vickers Shipbuilding Group Ltd
Number of Negatives	94
Print Status	Partially printed
Other Material	Photographic prints and photograph albums
Access	Partially catalogued

The vessels depicted were built by Charles Mitchell & Co, Sir W G Armstrong, Mitchell & Co Ltd, Sir W G Armstrong, Whitworth & Co Ltd and Vickers Armstrong Ltd, Newcastle. Worthy of particular note are two series of negatives showing the Chinese cruiser *Chih Yuan* immediately prior to her launch in 1886 and the launch of the aircraft carrier *Victorious* on 14 September 1939. The majority are portraits of completed vessels, either in the Tyne or on trials. Three negatives show an Armstrong 16in. Mk.I gun and mounting, manufactured for installation in the battleships *Nelson* (1925) and *Rodney* (1925). Twenty relate to ship repair/ refitting at the company's

Palmers Hebburn or Palmers Jarrow yards.

One negative only has a Barrow connection. It should be stated that the negative collection forms a very small part of the total amount of material donated by the Vickers Group.

204   Villiers.

Acquisition	Purchased from Mrs Nancie Villiers
Photographer	Mr Alan J Villiers
Number of Negatives	20,000
Print Status	Partially printed
Other Material	Photographic prints and transparencies
Access	Partially catalogued

Alan Villiers was a founding father of the Museum's photographic archive. The collection reflects the great variety of Villiers' maritime endeavours, including his time with

Pulley-hauley Arab style on board the ghancha *Al Saieed*, under Captain Salim, en route from Matrah to Muscat, 1928-1930.
Collection: Vaughan NMM Neg. No. P34986

Stern view of a boom beached at Kharag in July 1929.
Collection: Vaughan NMM Neg. No. P34631

The starboard side of the main deck of the Finnish four-master *Parma* (1902) looking forward as a sea breaks aboard.
Collection: Villiers NMM Neg. No. N61453

Above left: The great bulk of the aircraft carrier *Victorious* sliding into the waters of the Tyne from No. 3 Berth of Vickers-Armstrong's Newcastle shipyard on 14 September 1939. Twenty months later she commissioned for service.
Collection: Vickers NMM Neg. No. G13055

Above right: View aft from the main crosstrees of the ship *Grace Harwar* (1889) on passage in 1929, looking towards the mizzen mast. The mizzen topgallant sail has blown out and the royal is being furled.
Collection: Villiers NMM Neg. No. N61253

Below: On 6 June 1896 two Norwegian fishermen, George Harbo and Frank Samuelson, set out to row from New York to England. They arrived in the Isles of Scilly 55 days later after rowing 3,250 miles in their 18-foot boat, the *Fox*. This photograph shows the pair soon after arrival.
Collection: Ward-Jackson NMM Neg. No. C299

the Norwegian Ross Sea Whaling expedition in 1923–24; his long voyages under sail in the *Herzogin Cecilie* (1902) in 1928, *Grace Harwar* (1889) in 1929 and *Parma* (1902) in 1932–33; his pioneering work in sail training in the *Joseph Conrad* (1882); his voyages in Arab dhows; his war service in landing craft; his voyage with the Portuguese cod-fishing fleet and his captaincy of the *Mayflower* replica built in 1956. Other subjects Villiers recorded included a trip in 1958 in the Grimsby trawler *Samarian* (1957) to the fishing grounds off the Faeroes, the making of the same year's film 'John Paul Jones' and the Tall Ships Race of 1964 (Lisbon-Bermuda). Over 800 negatives dealing with the merchant sailing ships of the 1928 to 1933 period have been catalogued. The remainder of the collection has undergone preliminary sorting only and is not readily available.

In the late 1930s Lieutenant D W Waters RN was serving on the China Station and attempted to record photographically the various types of local craft. This is a fishing vessel which operated out of Tolo Harbour, Hong Kong.
Collection: Waters
NMM Neg. No. P34055

205 Walker.

Acquisition	Donated by Mr Len Walker
Photographer	Mr Len Walker
Number of Negatives	11
Print Status	Negatives only
Access	Fully catalogued

The 1927 excursion paddle steamer *Princess Elizabeth* is shown on 4 June 1970 as a floating restaurant. Six of the negatives were taken when she berthed at a quayside, possibly Albion Wharf, at Woolwich and mainly show details of the ship. The remainder show her in charge of tugs off Albion Wharf and bound up the Thames for St Katherine's Wharf. Mr Walker was a photographer on the NMM staff.

206 Ward-Jackson.

Acquisition	Copied from photographs lent by Mr C H Ward-Jackson
Number of Negatives	23
Print Status	Printed
Other Material	Photographic prints
Access	Numbered, Sorted, Identified

These negatives are mainly of schooners but also include a barquentine and a pilot cutter. Known locations are Fowey, Looe, Charlestown and Teignmouth. Other images include the wreck of the five-masted auxiliary schooner *Capitaine Remy* (1918), cargo being discharged from an unidentified schooner at Pont, near Fowey, the coastguards of Polperro in 1902 and two Norwegian fishermen who rowed the Atlantic in 1896.

207 Waters, D W.

Acquisition	Donated by Lieutenant-Commander D W Waters RN
Photographer	Lieutenant Commander D W Waters RN
Number of Negatives	658
Print Status	Printed
Other Material	Photographic prints, photograph albums and transparencies
Access	Numbered, Sorted, Identified

This is by far the most comprehensive collection of Chinese junk and sampan negatives that the Museum holds. It embraces different types of these craft from as far north as Wei-Hai-Wei and Tsingtao to as far south as Singapore and Penang, with the different types to be seen at Hong Kong and Shanghai very well represented in between.
The negatives were taken during the period 1937–38 when the photographer was serving with 824 Squadron of the Fleet Air Arm aboard HMS *Eagle* (1918). Whenever time permitted, Commander Waters sailed in junks on the Chinese coast, submitting articles on them to 'The Mariner's Mirror', the journal of the Society for Nautical Research.
The Museum also has four photograph albums of junks, presented by Commander Waters, who after leaving the Royal Navy in 1950 continued as an Admiralty Historian until 1960. He then joined the staff of the National Maritime Musem and retired in 1978 as Deputy Director.

208   Watkins, D B.

Acquisition	Purchased from Mrs F Watkins
Photographer	Mr D B Watkins
Number of Negatives	48
Print Status	Negatives only
Other Material	Photographic prints, transparencies and postcards
Access	Numbered, Identified

Ferries and excursion vessels in the 1950s and 1960s are depicted around the British Isles, chiefly in the Irish Sea and Channel Islands, in Norwegian coastal waters and on the Swiss lakes.

209   Watkins, T C.

Acquisition	Presented by Mr T C Watkins
Photographer	Engineer Commander B J Watkins
Number of Negatives	73
Print Status	Printed
Other Material	Photographic prints
Access	Numbered, Sorted, Identified

These negatives date from 1891 to 1894 when the photographer was serving on HMS *Porpoise* (1886) on the China Station. As well as his own ship, subjects covered by Mr

Top: The comfortable but cluttered appearance of the commander's cabin of the China Station flagship *Imperieuse* in the period 1891–94. HMS *Imperieuse* was an armoured cruiser completed in 1886 and sold in 1913.
**Collection: T C Watkins
NMM Neg. No. P27622**

Middle: Built by Elder at Glasgow, 1876–78, the steel corvette HMS *Comus* served her entire sea-going career on foreign stations, principally the Pacific and the North America and West Indies Stations. The dry dock at Esquimalt, British Columbia is the location for this photograph, dated 1895–98.
**Collection: Weinstein
NMM Neg. No. N11548**

Bottom: The Type 41 anti-aircraft frigate HMS *Lynx* under way off Puerto Rico in the West Indies in mid-1966. The *Lynx* was launched in 1955 and sold out of service in 1982. The photographer was embarked in the frigate *Ursa*.
**Collection: Wettern
NMM Neg. No. P39162**

Watkins include Hong Kong (both harbour and town), Hankow, Nanking, Foochow and Amoy in China, Petropavlovsk in Russia and Iliuliuk Harbour in the Aleutian Islands. (The *Porpoise* was engaged in patrolling the sealing grounds in the Bering Sea during part of this commission).

Officers' cabins are shown on what is thought to be HMS *Imperieuse* (1883), the station flagship. Also depicted is a monument erected on Sand Island in the Pescadores group to those who perished in the wreck of the P & O liner *Bokhara* (1873) in October 1892. There is also a depiction of the officers of HMS *Tartar* (1886) sometime between 1899 and 1901.

210   Wayne.

Acquisition	Presented by Mr Francis Wayne
Number of Negatives	971
Print Status	Partially printed
Other Material	Photographic prints
Access	Partially catalogued

Francis Wayne was interested in merchant sailing ships of all types and his negatives, mainly taken in the 1920s and 1930s, reflect this interest. As well as ocean-going vessels such as ships, barques and schooners, he also photographed Thames spritsail barges, various types of fishing vessels and a few yachts.

He appears to have concentrated mainly on the south-east of England, travelling as far west as Poole and north to Kings Lynn. One of his trips took him to Finland via Copenhagen and another excursion saw him visiting Naples, Port Said and Cyprus. A small number of negatives were taken on the west coast of Scotland.

211   Weinstein.

Acquisition	Gift of Mr R Weinstein
Number of Negatives	11
Print Status	Printed
Access	Fully catalogued

Taken at Esquimalt, British Columbia in the 1890s, these negatives show the corvette HMS *Comus* (1878), under repair and the armoured cruiser HMS *Imperieuse* (1883).

212   Wettern.

Acquisition	Gift of Mrs G Wettern
Photographer	Mr D Wettern
Number of Negatives	2,689
Print Status	Negatives only
Other Material	Photographic prints, photograph albums and transparencies
Access	Sorted

Desmond Wettern was a well-known champion of the Royal Navy. In 1961 he became the first naval correspondent of 'The Sunday Telegraph', moving to 'The Daily Telegraph' in 1975. His position enabled him to visit warships of various nationalities during exercises of the western powers. He also took photographs of Royal Navy ships attending to their normal duties in places as diverse as the North Sea, the West Indies, Singapore and Hong Kong. His photography covers the period 1961–80 and is in 35mm format. Among the many exercises covered are 'Midlink' in 1963, 'Polar Express' in 1968, 'Strong Express' in 1972 and 'Ocean Safari' in 1977. As well as British and foreign warships he also photographed ocean weather ships at work in 1962, the nuclear powered cargo ship *Savannah* in 1963 and the sail training brig *Royalist* in 1973.

213   Wheeler.

Acquisition	Copied from photographs donated by Mrs J Wheeler
Photographer	Dr J F G Wheeler
Number of Negatives	32
Print Status	Negatives only
Access	Numbered, Identified

These images were taken during the Discovery Expedition of 1925-27 to South Georgia and are principally concerned with whaling from Grytviken.

The Great White South Jazz Band, at Grytviken, South Georgia c.1926. These are members of the *Discovery* expedition of 1925–27 which sought a basis for regulating the whaling industry in the Southern Ocean.
Collection: Wheeler
NMM Neg. No. C4072/15

214 Wicksteed.

Acquisition	Donated by Mr O H Wicksteed FRPS
Photographer	Mr O H Wicksteed FRPS
Number of Negatives	58
Print Status	Negatives only
Other Material	Photographic prints
Access	Numbered

Mr O H Wicksteed took most of the negatives in the Edinburgh ports of Leith, Granton and Fisherrow. His interest was merchant sailing ships and sail training ships. Ten negatives were taken in the Deal area of Kent showing Deal galleys. This collection dates from 1922 to 1934.

215 Wilde.

Acquisition	Copied from photographs donated by Commander J O S Wilde RN Rtd
Number of Negatives	73
Print Status	Printed
Other Material	Photographic prints
Access	Numbered, Sorted, Identified

Lieutenant J S Wilde was gunnery officer of HMS *Terrible* (1895) during her 1898–1902 commission, when she sailed from Portsmouth for the Cape Station under the command of Captain Percy Scott. She disembarked her Naval Brigade and some guns at Durban and they were used at the Battle of Colenso and the relief of Ladysmith. The ship then moved to the China Station where her Naval Brigade was used during the Boxer Rebellion. Her crew also assisted in the salvage of the dredger *Canton River* (1897) at Hong Kong in 1901. She returned to Portsmouth in September 1902. The collection contains views of the Naval Brigade operating in South Africa and China and of life on board the *Terrible* at this time.

216 Williamson.

Number of Negatives	23
Print Status	Partially printed
Access	Partially catalogued

These negatives were taken in the mid-1930s in London and in the Mediterranean. They include sailing vessels such as the barques *L'Avenir* (1908) and *Pestalozzi* (1884), and the brigantine *Gilda* (1909).

217 Willis.

Acquisition	Donated by H C Willis
Number of Negatives	23
Print Status	Printed
Other Material	Photographic prints
Access	Fully catalogued

Warships laid up at Sheerness in 1919 or 1920 form the subject of this collection. Ships included are battleships, cruisers, monitors and depot ships but the negatives are of poor quality.

218 Woodspring Museum.

Acquisition	Transferred from Woodspring Museum, Weston-Super-Mare (Miss K Evans)
Number of Negatives	23
Print Status	Negatives only
Access	Numbered

Donated to the Woodspring Museum by Mr C Harrison and transferred in 1988, this collection depicts Irish Sea ferries and British warships in the first decade of the twentieth century. A number of the negatives were taken at Holyhead. The warships are part of the Channel Fleet.

The Naval Brigade from HM cruiser *Terrible* with a 4.7-in. gun at the Battle of Colenso on 15 December 1899, during the Boer War. Naval guns and gunners were instrumental in lifting the siege of Ladysmith.
Collection: Wilde NMM Neg. No. C7195/13

219 Wright.

Acquisition	Copied from photographs lent by Mr E V Wright MBE
Number of Negatives	17
Print Status	Printed
Other Material	Photographic prints
Access	Numbered, Sorted, Identified

On Friday, 26 June 1914 King George V, accompanied by Queen Mary, visited Hull and performed the opening ceremony of the new Hull Joint Dock. The negatives show vessels of the Royal Navy's Seventh Destroyer Flotilla berthed in the dock, the Trinity House yacht *Irene* (1890) which acted as the royal yacht, the royal dais at No. 3 Quay and scenes outside Hull Town Hall.

220 Yarwood.

Acquisition	Gift of Mr A Yarwood
Number of Negatives	11
Print Status	Printed
Access	Numbered, Sorted, Identified

The negatives received from Mr Yarwood were taken on board the Glasgow-built, steel ship *Tamar* (1889) in the period 1913–22. Seven of the negatives show the masts and sails only, whereas the remaining four also show some of the deck. They were all taken when the ship was at sea.

Top: The Italian brigantine *Gilda* (1909), of Syracuse, setting sail on her departure from Salerno early in the morning of 26 April 1937.
Collection: Williamson
NMM Neg. No. N41725

Left: King George V disembarking from the Trinity House Yacht *Irene* for the official opening of the Hull Joint Dock on 26 June 1914. In the dock basin are units of the Seventh Destroyer Flotilla.
Collection: Wright
NMM Neg. No. D1690

Indexes

The facade of the P & O Steam Navigation Co's Passenger Office at 15 and 16 Cockspur Street, London SW1. The photograph was taken in July 1952.
Collection: P & O NMM Neg. No. G4399

The quartermaster at the wheel of the passenger liner *Kenya* (1951). The *Kenya* was built for the British-India Steam Navigation Co for their East Africa service and had not yet sailed on her maiden voyage when this photograph was taken on 16 July 1951.
Collection: P & O NMM Neg. No. P39173

Person and Corporate Body Index

This index includes both photographed and photographer, as well as the companies whose vessels or yards are shown.

Alan Villiers, seated by the forecastle rail of the Finnish ship *Grace Harwar* (1889) on passage from Wallaroo to Glasgow, via Queenstown, in 1929.
Collection: Villiers NMM Neg. No. N61226

Seen here on 26 May 1967, in the ship's wheelhouse and standing at the engine-room telegraph, is the master of the educational cruise ship *Nevasa*, built for service as a troopship in 1956.
Collection: P & O
NMM Neg. No. P39171

Place Index

This index incorporates geographical locations and specific sites, such as; lighthouses, docks, ports, harbours and quays. See also the Subject Index for these topics.

This photograph dates from the late 1860s and shows the harbour at Torquay, in Devon. At the quayside, discharging a cargo of coal, to be taken away by the waiting horses and carts, is the brigantine *Summerside*, built on Prince Edward Island, Canada, in 1865.
Collection: Bedford NMM Neg. No. C9371

The Langton Graving Dock, Liverpool, on 19 April 1895. In the dock is Cunard's steamship *Cherbourg*, built in 1875 for the cargo service to Mediterranean ports.
Collection: London, Midland & Scottish Railway NMM Neg. No. G3608

Built in 1842 at Amlwch, the schooner *Catherine* dominates this 1891 photograph of Carnarvon Castle (Caernarfon), viewed from across the river Seiont. Slate is being exported from the wharf.
Collection: Frith NMM Neg. No. G4362

This is the harbour of Douglas, Isle of Man, on 1 September 1904. Alongside is the Manx Steam Trading Co's cargo steamship *Tyrconnel*, built in 1892 and registered at Castletown, on the island. Among other items of cargo the ship is discharging a commodity in barrels from the after hold.
Collection: Mullett NMM Neg. No. P39877

Emigrants for America on board the Hamburg-Amerika liner *Deutschland* (1900) at the Prince of Wales pier, Dover in July 1906. The ship was damaged in a collision leaving Dover and her passengers completed their voyage in another vessel.
Collection: Adams NMM Neg. No. N19706

Subject Index

This index covers a multiplicity of topics. Here can be found references to ceremonies, decks and interiors, fishing related activities, fleets, life at sea, racing, lighthouses, docks, shipbuilding, repair activity, events and so on.

In the foreground to this photograph of the Dumbarton shipyard of William Denny & Bros. is the Australasian United S.N. Co's passenger-cargo liner *Kyarra*, fitting out early in 1903. The *Kyarra* was torpedoed and lost off Anvil Point, on the Devon coast, on 26 May 1918.
Collection: Denny NMM Neg. No. D4304A

Refitting a ship involves many skills and trades. John I Thornycroft & Co employed a large number of craftsmen to make and repair furniture. This 1921 photograph of the upholstery repair department at Woolston shipyard show some of these men at work.
Collection: Thornycroft NMM Neg. No. G9899

Before the advent of oil-fired boilers, taking on bunkers was a laborious and dirty task which usually involved the entire crew. The cruiser *Amethyst* is taking on a full load of coal in 1905.
Collection: Perkins NMM Neg. No. N7835

An unfortunate passenger undergoes the ritual of the crossing-the-line ceremony in this photograph taken during the maiden voyage of the Union-Castle liner *Transvaal Castle* in January 1962. After attention from the 'barber', seen here on the left, the initiate would be ducked in the pool.
Collection: Union-Castle NMM Neg. No. P39166

This early photograph, made on calotype paper negative dates, in all probability, from the last quarter of 1845 and is very likely to be the work of William Henry Fox Talbot himself. The view is across Plymouth harbour from Mount Edgecumbe, looking towards the Royal William Victualling Yard.
Collection: Talbot NMM Neg. No. 4411/B

Vessel Names Index

This is by no means a comprehensive list of the vessels depicted. Vessels have been selected where they may have been important to a collection or to reflect the variety.

A

Achilles (1863) [battleship, HMS], 72
Achilles (1932) [cruiser, HMS], 55
Ackworth (1889) [general cargo vessel], 175
Agamemnon (1855) [3 masted ship], 76
Agincourt (1865) [battleship, HMS], 193
Agincourt (1913) [battleship, HMS], 41
Ajax (1912) [battleship, HMS], 151
Alarm (1892) [gunboat, HMS], 171
Alarm (1898) [barge], 76
Alaska (fl.1923) [crabber], 89
Albert (1906) [barge], 44
Alberta (1907) [yacht, HMS], 86
Albion (1900) [barge], 89
Alexander Tulloch (1912) [lifeboat], 24
Almirante Cochrane (1874) [battleship, Chile], 76
Amerigo Vespucci (1930) [training ship, Italy], 131
Anglo (1960) [tanker], 88
Apollo (1954) [general cargo vessel], 18
Aquitania (1914) [liner], 13, 152
Arethusa (1913) [cruiser, HMS], 81
Argus (1939) [schooner], 204
Ariadne (1898) [cruiser, HMS], 105
Arlanza (1960) [liner], 152
Assaroe (1893) [passenger], 84
Audrey (1897) [paddle steamer], 184
Aurora (1913) [cruiser, HMS], 81
Austral (1881) [liner], 46
Australia (1911) [battlecruiser, HMAS], 57
Avon (1896) [destroyer, HMS], 219
Avon (1943) [frigate, HMS], 88

B

Balantia (1909) [liner], 110
Ban Righ (1870) [general cargo vessel], 76
Banshee (1894) [destroyer, HMS], 36
Barbain (1940) [boom gate defence vessel, HMS], 212
Barbara (1926) [general cargo vessel], 74
Barham (1914) [battleship, HMS], 41, 77, 137
Basset (1935) [trawler, HMS], 55
Bellerophon (1907) [battleship, HMS], 21, 40, 41
Bellona (1909) [cruiser, HMS], 83
Benlarig (1904) [liner], 76
Berry Head (1944) [depot & repair ship, HMS], 132
Bessemer (1874) [ferry], 76
Birmingham City (1946) [general cargo vessel], 88
Black Prince (1861) [battleship, HMS], 173
Blanche F Sigman (1943) [hospital ship], 161
Bloemfontein (1934) [liner], 161
Blonde (1863) [general cargo vessel], 76
Booker Vanguard (1963) [general cargo vessel], 161
Borderglen (1913) [tender, HMS], 170
Boston City (1920) [liner], 39
Braemar (1952) [liner], 102
Brahmaputra (1957) [frigate, India], 2

Britannia (1885) [cable ship], 76
Britannia (1953) [yacht, HMS], 11, 132
Britannic (1930) [liner], 137
British Norness (1973) [tanker], 161
British Science (1931) [tanker], 103
British Trader (1921) [tanker], 103
Buzzard (1887) [training ship, HMS], 87

C

C109 (1865) [coaling hulk, HMS], 193
Caltex Canberra (1953) [tanker], 192
Caltex Dublin (1945) [tanker], 192
Caltex Manchester (1953) [tanker], 192
Cambria (1897) [ferry], 218
Cambrian (1960) [tug], 18
Cambrook (1967) [dredger], 18
Campbell (1918) [destroyer, HMS], 83
Canada (1913) [battleship, HMS], 41
Canberra (1961) [liner], 145
Canterbury (1915) [cruiser, HMS], 106
Canton River (1897) [dredger], 215
Cap Pilar (1911) [barquentine], 134
Captaine Remy (1918) [schooner], 206
Carmenta (1879) [schooner], 94
Ceylon (1858) [liner], 76
Chidambaram (1966) [liner], 3
Chih Yuan (1886) [cruiser, China], 203
Chimborazo (1871) [liner], 46
City of Christiana (1921) [liner], 103
City of Glasgow (1901) [lifeboat], 50
City of Glasgow (1958) [liner], 161
City of Lincoln (1938) [liner], 103
Clan Chattan (1944) [liner], 11
Clan MacIver (1921) [liner], 103
Clan Mackenzie (1917) [liner], 103
Collingwood (1908) [battleship, HMS], 83
Collingwood Dickson (1889) [tender], 164
Colorado Star (1952) [general cargo vessel], 196
Colossus (1882) [battleship, HMS], 175
Comte de Smet de Naeyer (1904) [3-masted ship], 116
Comus (1878) [corvette, HMS], 211
Conquest (1915) [cruiser, HMS], 106
Courageous (1916) [aircraft carrier, HMS], 27
Cricket (1915) [gunboat, HMS], 83
Crystal Stream (1983) [yacht], 61
Cumberland (1926) [cruiser, HMS], 55
Cunard Countess (1975) [liner], 161
Cushendall (1904) [general cargo vessel], 66
Cygnet (1931) [destroyer, HMS], 55

D

Dacia (1867) [cable ship], 141
Danae (1918) [cruiser, HMS], 92
Danmark (1932) [training ship, Denmark], 73
Dannebrog (1901) [barge], 134
Danube (1869) [passenger & cargo vessel], 209
Dartmothian (1919) [tug], 104
Dauntless (1918) [cruiser, HMS], 217
De Grasse (1924) [liner], 146

Dee Why (1970) [ferry], 161
Delhi (1918) [cruiser, HMS], 203
Despatch (1919) [cruiser, HMS], 101
Devastation (1871) [battleship, HMS], 218
Dido (1896) [cruiser, HMS], 182
Dido (1939) [cruiser, HMS], 161
Discovery (1901) [expedition ship], 35, 213
Discovery II (1929) [expedition ship], 51
Dragon (1917) [cruiser, HMS], 168
Drayton Grange (1901) [liner], 91
Dreadnought (1906) [battleship, HMS], 21, 27, 136, 154
Dresden (1917) [cruiser, Germany], 49
Dronning Ingrid (1950) [ferry], 102
Droxford (1954) [seaward defence boat, HMS], 132
Duke of Devonshire (1896) [paddle steamer], 119
Dulwich (1957) [collier], 179
Dumra (1922) [liner], 39
Duncan (1880) [tug], 56

E

Eagle (1918) [aircraft carrier, HMS], 138
Earl of Zetland (1877) [ferry], 183
Edavana (1911) [troopship], 133
Elizabeth (1838) [ketch], 150
Ellora (1911) [hospital ship], 133
Emperor of India (1913) [battleship, HMS], 151
Empire Frome (1948) [general cargo vessel], 134
Empire Glory (1943) [general cargo vessel], 125
Empire Maccabe (1943) [tanker], 161
Empress of Australia (1914) [liner], 124
Empress of France (1913) [liner], 98, 124
Endeavour (1934) [yacht], 16
Endurance (1912) [expedition ship], 87
Endurance (1956) [patrol vessel, HMS], 132
Erebus (1916) [monitor, HMS], 217
Erin (1913) [battleship, HMS], 41, 217
Eskimo (1910) [ferry], 182
Eugenio C (1966) [liner], 174
Euryalus (1901) [cruiser, HMS], 218

F

Fantome (1901) [sloop, HMS], 105
Fathomer (1941) [fishing vessel], 73
Flamingo (1939) [sloop, HMS], 203
Fleurus (1919) [expedition ship], 51
Flying Cloud (1918) [yacht], 42
Flying Cloud (1927) [yacht], 42
Formidable (1825) [training ship, HMS], 78
Formidable (1898) [battleship, HMS], 54
Formosa (1883) [barque], 76
Fortis (1898) [barge], 44
Foudroyant (1798) [training ship, HMS], 169
Frances and Jane (1878) [barquentine], 129
Fraser (1931) [destroyer, HMCS], 55
Fredericksburg (1975) [drill ship], 3
Fuglen (1884) [barquentine], 89

The *Chigwell* was one of the first ocean-going oil tankers. The vessel was built at Sunderland as a dry-cargo ship in 1883 and converted to carry oil in bulk to the order of Alfred Suart, a pioneer British owner of oil tankers.
Collection: Gould NMM Neg. No. G810

Members of the port forecastle of the *Passat* (1911), one of the last deep-sea, square-rigged merchantmen. The photograph was taken by Anne Stanley in March 1949.
Collection: Stanley NMM Neg. No. P8496

The Royal Fleet Auxiliary oiler *War Bahadur* laid up on 30 March 1938. Her bridge was destroyed by a freak wave in the Atlantic in January 1938 and she was escorted to safety by the destroyer HMS *Wolverine*.
Collection: Perkins NMM Neg. No. N4756

Members of the crew of the Union-Castle liner *Tintagel Castle* (1896) take the parts of King Neptune and his entourage at a crossing-the-line ceremony at the turn of the century. On passenger ships the boisterous celebration of passing the Equator, common on cargo vessels, was moderated in deference to passengers' sensibilities.
Collection: Nautical Photo Agency NMM Neg. No. N47734

The stern and quadruple screws of the Cunard passenger liner *Aquitania* during the second half of May 1914, shortly before the ship commenced her maiden voyage from Liverpool to New York. The *Aquitania*'s turbines produced 62,000 SHP, giving the ship a speed of 23 knots.
Collection: Bedford Lemere
NMM Neg. No. G10800

Vessel Type and Design Class Index

Types can be sought under their specific type, ie: frigate or under a wider genre such as: fighting/service/cargo/ recreation/sailing/exploration/research/fishing/hunting/training vessel or native craft. It is not always easy to pigeonhole a ship type; a sailing yacht, for instance, could be classified either as a recreational vessel or a sailing vessel with equal validity. Therefore, terms in this index are generally inverted so that the type will be listed as well; for example, 'light cruiser' will be found under 'cruiser, light'. References to groupings of warships and merchant shipping (as opposed to specific types) can be found under warships or merchant vessels in this index and/or under general terms in the Subject Index.

174

Affectionately known as 'Smokey Joes', the Hunt class minesweepers were the backbone of Britain's mine warfare forces between the wars. The Clyde-built *Craigie* is under way on the Clyde in 1918.
Collection: Perkins NMM Neg. No. G5388

The most numerous, and famous, of World War II war-emergency standard cargo ships were the Liberty ships, of which type more than 2,700 were completed in America between 1942 and 1945. Seen in this photograph, under way at Southampton on 4 December 1943, is the *Ignace Paderewski*, a Liberty ship built at Los Angeles in 1943.
Collection: Admiralty NMM Neg. No. P22978

The 'Victory' type standard turbine steamship *Cherry Victory* (1945) off northern Sumatra in October 1969. She is at anchor, discharging her cargo of iron ore, after grounding whilst on a voyage from Mormugao to Keelung.
Collection: Airfoto NMM Neg. No. P40877

Passengers boarding the British-India liner *Mulbera* (1922) in the Royal Albert Dock, London, on 21 June 1952.
Collection: P & O NMM Neg. No. P39174

The Thames sailing barge *Centaur*, winner of the Thames barge match of 6 June 1899.
She is wearing her winner's pennants.
Collection: Gould NMM Neg. No. G1351

How to contact the National Maritime Museum

For all information enquiries contact:
The Historic Photographs Section
Maritime Information Centre
National Maritime Museum
Greenwich
London SE10 9NF
Tel: 0181–858 4422   Fax: 0181–312 6632

Selection

Where negatives have been printed, these prints will be arranged according to subject. For example, all photographs of HMS *Hood* will be found together, irrespective of the collections in which individual negatives originated. This applies to all photographs of every ship type. Topographical photographs are arranged in a similar manner, following a progression along the coastline, first of the British Isles and then on around the world. Thus, every photograph of the River Tyne included in the collection will be found together. There are further series which address particular topics, such as life in the Royal Navy, travellers by sea, uniforms, etc.,.

Once acquired by the Museum, the integrity of an individual collection is maintained through its acquisition record and the allocation of a block of numbers by which the negatives are identified. It would be impossibly unwieldy and inconvenient to maintain the resulting prints according to their collection of origin; to facilitate consultation of the photographs these are spread through the archive, as described, according to subject matter. In those cases where a negative remains unprinted, many will be recorded in the Historic Photograph Section's subject indexes: many, perforce, are unavailable for the time being. Negatives which have been catalogued by inclusion within an index, and allocated a negative number may be printed to order.

Top: An impression of power – six of the nine 16-inch guns which constitute the main armament of the battleship HMS *Nelson*. The negative was made by Stephen Cribb in the late 1920s.
Collection: Cribb NMM Neg. No. N22380

Middle: Large numbers of drifters were built for the Admiralty in 1917–19. Among the many mundane tasks that they undertook was that of tender to the capital ships of the navy. Here the *Horizon* of 1918 is attending the battlecruiser *Hood* in 1931.
Collection: Perkins NMM Neg. No. N4474

Bottom: During World War II many passenger liners were used as infantry landing ships for special operations. The Dutch *Marnix Van Sint Aldegonde* of 1930 was so used in November 1942 for the allied landings in North Africa; Operation Torch.
Collection: Admiralty NMM Neg. No. AD12705/A

The destroyer *Blackwater* was launched by Laird Brothers at Birkenhead in July 1903 and this view shows her on trials before the fitting of any armament. The builder's yard number 652 can be seen on her bow.
Collection: Perkins NMM Neg. No. G5261

Availability and Viewing of Photographs

Contact the Historic Photographs Section in writing for information about historic photographs and respective quotations for reproductions. We endeavour to respond to all enquiries by letter within 28 days. The Section may be visited and the collection of photographic prints consulted during weekdays, by appointment only. Enquiries by letter or telephone are accepted but in each case requests must be limited to modest proportions. Professional researchers, approved by the Museum, may be employed by those wishing to find large

This aerial view is of the North Port, Port Kelang, Malaysia c.1974, showing part of the extensive container handling facility at Malaysia's principal port. Alongside is the Ben Line container ship *City of Edinburgh* (1973).
Collection: Airfoto
NMM Neg. No. P40963

numbers of images. Extensive indexes to the collection are held by the curators, giving full descriptions of photographs of ships, topographical subjects and life at sea. It must be stressed that the Historic Photographs Collection is not a photo library and does not offer the services of one. Only in exceptional circumstances is it possible to examine original negatives.

Ordering Photographs

Black and white photographs or 35 mm slides may be provided for private study or research and we endeavour to dispatch orders within 28 days of payment. Prints and 35 mm slides may not be used for reproduction, resale or public display, unless a separate agreement is entered into with the Museum. **Orders for photographs should always quote the unique negative number (NMM. Neg. No.) and should be addressed to the Photo Sales Section.**

Ordering Photographs from this Publication

To purchase photographs directly from the Guide, please specify the negative number which resides in the caption by the photograph and the size of the black and white print in inches (7x5)/(10x8)/(16x12)/(20x16).

The photographs shown in the Guide are representative of the broad range of subjects held by the Museum. In this publication the originals of all photographs are black and white. Please be sure to quote the negative number when enquiring about a specific photograph. If enquiring about a collection please use the collection name rather than number.

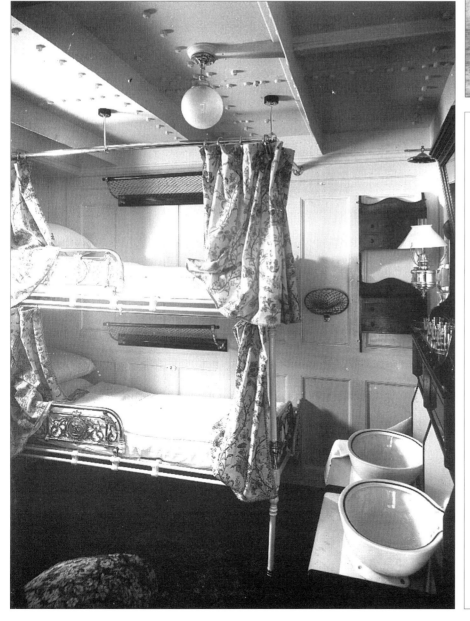

Above: Heaving the lead on board the New Zealand Shipping Company's passenger/cargo liner *Rangitiki* in 1937. This vessel served the company from 1929 to 1962.
Collection: Nautical Photo Agency
NMM Neg. No. N47546

Top, left: Thornycroft's, in addition to shipbuilding, were ship repairers and refitters. Here a new starboard low pressure stern tube for the Cunard passenger liner *Mauretania* is being bored out in the heavy machine shop at Woolston in 1920.
Collection: Thornycroft
NMM Neg. No. G9895

Left: A Second Class cabin on board the *Saxonia* (1900) of the Cunard Line.
Collection: Bedford Lemere
NMM Neg. No. G10539

Following page:
Top: On 11 September 1911 the steamship *Papanui* (1899), outward bound from London to Fremantle with 364 emigrant passengers, put into Jamestown Harbour, on the island of St Helena, with the coal she carried as bunkers in No. 3 hold on fire. The fire could not be controlled and the ship became a total loss.
Collection: Nautical Photo Agency
NMM Neg. No. P834

Bottom: The new fish factory stern trawler *Lord Nelson* on arrival at Hull from her German builders in 1961. She is being assisted into the lock by the local steam tug *Kiero*, built by Richard Dunston Limited at Thorne in 1943 as the *TID 44* for the Ministry of War Transport.
Collection: Hull
NMM Neg. No. P33697

Pearson Education Limited
Pearson
KAO Two
KAO Park
Harlow
Essex
CM17 9NA

and Associated Companies throughout the world.

ISBN 9781292240107

Peter Pan © Great Ormond Street Hospital for Children
Illustrations © Richard Gray 2001; p32 Bridget Dowty/GCI

This adaptation first published by
Penguin Books 2001
1 3 5 7 9 10 8 6 4 2

Retold by Marie Crook
Series Editor: Melanie Williams
Illustration by Richard Gray & Bridget Dowty
Design by Wendi Watson

Printed in China
SWTC/01

The moral right of the author and illustrator have been asserted

Published by Pearson Education Limited

For a complete list of titles available in the Pearson Story Readers series please write
to your local Pearson Education office or contact:
Pearson, KAO Two, KAO Park, Harlow, Essex, CM17 9NA

Answers for the Activities in this book are published in the free Pearson English Story
Readers Factsheet on the website, www.pearsonenglishreaders.com